Céad Míle :
of Ir

Welcome, fái

benvenuto,

Welcome to the newest edition of Ireland's Blue Book. Founded in 1974, we are a unique association comprising the country's finest Manor Houses, Castles, and Historic Hotels together with wonderful Restaurants, all over the island of Ireland. Each property has something different to offer in an enchanting and welcoming atmosphere.

For those of you seeking a scenic retreat or a gourmet getaway, there is somewhere perfect for you in our collection. For the more energetic among you, we have fishing, golf, cycling and equestrian pursuits. Included in our Blue Book are some very indulgent spas - if you want to be spoiled. You could combine business with pleasure and book your corporate occasions with us too. We have venues to cater for events of all tastes and sizes.

I would also like to welcome our new members, Ballyfin Demesne in Co. Laois; Bishop's Gate Hotel in Co. Derry/Londonderry; Butler House in Co. Kilkenny; Cahernane House Hotel in Co. Kerry; Dunowen House in Co. Cork; and The Hideaway at Dromquinna Manor in Co. Kerry. We are delighted to have them as part of the Blue Book Family.

With every good wish on behalf of all our members.

Simon O'Hara

Simon O'Hara
Chairperson of Ireland's Blue Book

HOW TO BOOK A BLUE BOOK HOUSE

Simply visit Ireland's Blue Book website and make your reservation/booking.

www.irelandsbluebook.com

Perhaps you are more comfortable dealing with a person rather than booking online. In this instance please contact the houses directly; they would love to hear from you. At the bottom of each page you will find the proprietor's name, address, telephone, email and website.

Reservations can also be made through your travel agent.

Contact details
Ireland's Blue Book
63 Fitzwilliam Square
Dublin 2, Ireland
D02N938

T +353 (0) 1 676 9914
E mail@irelandsbluebook.com
www.irelandsbluebook.com

AHERNE'S TOWNHOUSE

Open fires and the warmest of welcomes await you in this family run hotel in the historic walled port of Youghal. Rooms are spacious and stylishly furnished. The famous Seafood Bar and Restaurant specialises in the freshest of Seafood (Lobster, Oysters, Crab, Prawns, Black Sole, Monkfish & Turbot) our bar is renowned for its friendliness; you can enjoy a chat with the locals along with your Guinness and Seafood. Coeliac friendly meals served for 30 years. Available for Intimate Weddings /Private Parties. Civil Marriage approved.

Local attractions: Clock Gate Tower and other local attractions, Walking, Swimming, Sea Angling, Kayaking, Greyhound Racing, Jameson Heritage Centre, Fota Wildlife Park, Ardmore Cliff Walk, Blarney Castle, Waterford Crystal and Lismore Castle. Ballymaloe cookery school, Waterford Greenway.

Awards include:
Listed in the **Sunday Times** '50 best places to eat seafood in Ireland'.
Guardian Newspaper – 'One of the best breakfasts in Ireland'.
Georgina Campbell – 'Best brown bread award'.

Bedrooms **13**   Guesthouse ★ ★ ★ ★

**Aherne's, 163 North Main Street,
Youghal, Co.Cork**
T +353 (0)24 92424
info@ahernes.net
www.ahernes.com

Proprietor: The FitzGibbon Family
Open all year – except 4 days at Christmas.
Bed & Breakfast from €80 – €160 pps.
Single from €100 – €130.
Dinner served from 6pm to 9pm from €30.00.
Bar Food Service available Noon – 9pm daily.
Guide dogs welcome.
A Blue Book Voucher – complimentary upgrade where possible.

How to find:
Cork: 30 mins. (N25) Direction Rosslare.
Rosslare: 1.45hrs (N25).
Dublin: Take the N7 then the M7 onto the M9 to Waterford then take the N25 West to Youghal. 2.30hrs.

GPS coordinates
Lat: 51.957031634671
Long: -7.8518871130346

ARDTARA COUNTRY HOUSE

Set amidst 10 wooded acres, Ardtara is an elegant 19th century mansion in the heart of Northern Ireland. Just 15 minutes from Seamus Heaney HomePlace and within 45 minutes of both Belfast & Derry, the Giant's Causeway, the Antrim coast, Royal Portrush golf club and many Game of Thrones film locations, it's the perfect base from which to explore.

With an emphasis on using seasonal local produce and fruit and vegetables from our gardens, the award-winning restaurant serves exquisite dinners, a casual lounge menu, sumptuous afternoon teas and a superb Sunday lunch.

This charming house features a plethora of original Victorian features including working fireplaces in our bedrooms, which are uniquely designed in-keeping with the style of the house but with all the modern conveniences you would expect.

Recent Awards:
Best guest accommodation in Northern Ireland 2016/17 **(AA).**
Romantic Hotel of the Year 2017. Recommended in the **Michelin Guide.**

Bedrooms **9**   **Listed Heritage Property**

**Ardtara Country House & Restaurant,
8 Gorteade Road, Upperlands,
Co. L'Derry BT46 5SA**
T +44 (0)28 796 44490
info@ardtara.com
www.ardtara.com

Proprietors: Roulston & Orr Families
Open all year round.
House available for private hire.
Bed & Cooked Breakfast from £59.50.
Afternoon Tea, Dinner & Sunday Lunch available
to all by reservation.
Dinner 5.00 – 9.00pm a la carte.
Private dining room available by reservation.
Free wi-fi throughout.

How to find:
Take M2/M22/A6 north toward Derry/Londonderry.
7 miles past the Castledawson roundabout, take
A29 through Maghera. Continue on A29 towards
Coleraine for three miles out of Maghera to
the right turn on to B75. Proceed one mile into
Upperlands. Ardtara sign is on the left towards the
end of the village.

GPS coordinates
N 54.88297
W -6.636611

BALLYFIN DEMESNE

At the foot of the Slieve Bloom Mountains, just over an hour from Dublin, Ballyfin has long been admired as the most lavish Regency mansion in Ireland.

Decorated with Irish art and antiques from around the world, the interiors offer the same spirit of refined elegance that the early House reflected in the 1820s.

With just 20 bedrooms, Ballyfin has the flavour of a grand private house with the facilities of a five-star resort. Enjoy 614 acres of private parkland, 28-acre lake, ancient woods and follies, indoor swimming pool, gym and treatment rooms. A range of experiences are available such as coarse fishing, clay shooting, horse riding, falconry, and wine and whiskey tasting.

Travel and Leisure Awards 2018 – #2 Top Hotel in the World. #1 Top Resort Ireland, UK & Europe.
AA Hotel of the Year 2018.
Condé Nast Traveller Readers' Choice Awards 2016 – #1 Best Hotel in the World.

Bedrooms **20** and Gardener's Cottage   Hotel ★ ★ ★ ★ ★

Ballyfin Demesne
Ballyfin, Co.Laois
+353 (0)57 875 5866
reservations@ballyfin.com
www.ballyfin.com

General Manager: Damien Bastiat
Rates:
From €580.00 Bed & Breakfast
From €890.00 Full Board

How to find:
Ballyfin is located 10 minutes drive from Junction 18 of the M7 motorway. Leave the motorway at junction 18 signposted Tullamore and Mountrath. Follow signs for Mountrath, on entering Mountrath turn right at the traffic lights/ T-junction. Continue along this road to Ballyfin for approx 7.5km and you will reach the entrance gate on the left hand side signposted Ballyfin. Press the intercom at the gate for reception.

GPS coordinates
Latitude 53' 03'.666N
Longitude 007' 25'.134W

BALLYMALOE HOUSE COUNTRY HOUSE & RESTAURANT

Internationally renowned family-run country house built onto a castle. Surrounding gardens and farms provide the main ingredients for the restaurant. Minutes from the coast, and 20 miles from the historic city of Cork, bedrooms range from elegant and airy to charming and cosy.

Set in extensive gardens; during your visit enjoy farm walks, tennis, an outdoor swimming pool, croquet or an event at Ballymaloe Grainstore, visit the craft shop and café on site or enjoy the many surrounding East Cork attractions. The Ballymaloe Cookery School, also run by the Allen family, is 4 km from Ballymaloe House. Ballymaloe Grainstore is the ideal venue for conferences, weddings and private parties.

AA Notable Wine List / Quality Inspected 5* rating.
Condé Nast Traveler Gold list 100 World's Best Hotels.
Food & Wine Ireland's Top restaurants.
Georgina Campbell Best breakfasts in Ireland.
Food & Wine Farm & Sea to Plate Award 2018

Bedrooms **30**   Guesthouse ★ ★ ★ ★

**Ballymaloe House, Shanagarry,
Co.Cork, P25 Y070**
T +353 (0)21 465 2531
res@ballymaloe.ie
www.ballymaloe.ie
www.ballymaloegrainstore.com
www.ballymaloefestivals.com
#Ballymaloe - Facebook / Twitter / Instagram

Proprietors: The Allen Family
Closed: December 24th – 29th December 2018
and January 6th – 1st February 2019.
Bed & Breakfast per room.
Low season from €215.
High season from €270.
Service charge optional.

Dinner €75, from 6.30 – 9.30pm.
All major credit cards accepted.
Children welcome.

How to find:
From Cork take N25 east. Then take R630 and R631. We are 2 miles beyond Cloyne on the Ballycotton road. From Waterford take N25 west to Castlemartyr. In Ladysbridge take care to follow signs to Cloyne, we are 5 miles from Ladysbridge on the Cloyne Road.

GPS coordinates
Latitude: 51.865083
Longitude: -8.075021

BARBERSTOWN CASTLE

Formerly the home of Eric Clapton and welcoming guests for over 800 years, visitors to Barberstown will experience a very relaxing and welcoming Castle while enjoying great food, good wines, open log fires, luxury and exceptional personal service.

Use this unique Historic 13th Century Irish Castle as the ideal base from which to visit Dublin and explore Ireland's Ancient East. Enjoy 25 minutes carefree driving from, or to, Dublin Airport and Dublin City Centre.

Essential Day Trips include a visit to the Irish National Stud in Kildare Town. Enjoy a short drive through the Wicklow Mountains to explore Glendalough, Russborough and Powerscourt in County Wicklow, the Garden of Ireland. Newgrange (5,000 year old Megalithic site) and The Rock of Cashel are excellent day trips.

Awards include:
Best Historic Hotel of Europe Castle Winner.

Bedrooms **55 Ensuite**   Hotel ★ ★ ★ ★

Barberstown Castle, Straffan, Co.Kildare
T +353 (0)1 628 8157
F +353 (0)1 627 7027
info@barberstowncastle.ie
www.barberstowncastle.ie

Proprietor: Kenneth Healy
Open all year except three days at Christmas, January and February.
Bed & Breakfast Rates: €180 – €240 per night
Food served from 12pm until 10pm seven days a week.

GDS Codes:
HE DUBBCH, HE 29023, HE 30473, HE DUBBC

How to find:
Leave the airport and take the exit for the M50 South Bound. Leave the M50 at exit #7 (M4) and continue on the N4/M4 westward. Leave the M4 at Exit/Junction 7 (Straffan/Maynooth) and take the R407 to Straffan. (30 minutes - all Motorway). *Onward Journey:* Because the Castle is minutes from the M1, M50, M4 and M7 motorways, it is the most perfect starting point, or final evening, on your Blue Book tour of Ireland. This Castle is easy to Find but hard to Leave!

Belleek Castle, an iconic castle, gourmet restaurant, hotel and spectacular wedding venue on the Wild Atlantic Way.

The 1820s Neo-Gothic Castle is informal, cosy, warm, friendly, rich in decor and antiquities, with open log fires to light your steps back through this cultural adventure on the Wild Atlantic Way.

Enjoy a fine dining experience in our award winning Library Restaurant, have a drink in the Spanish Armada Bar or relax for brunch in Jack Fenn's. Explore Marshall Dorans collection of Fossils, Medieval Weapons & Armour.

Bespoke fairytale weddings designed to suit in the Medieval Banquet Hall. Unique, intimate and magical.

AA 2 Rosettes, Michelin Guide 2018, **Irish Hotel Awards:** Romantic Hotel of the Year 2018, **Good Eating Guide:** Best Restaurant in Connaught 2017, **RAI:** Best Hotel Restaurant 2016-2017.

Bedrooms **10**

Specialist accommodation **Historic Castle**

Belleek Castle,
Ballina, Co.Mayo
T +353 (0) 96 22 400
info@belleekcastle.eu
www.belleekcastle.com

Proprietors: The Doran Family
General Manager: Maya Nikolaeva
Closed January
Rates €170 – €290.

How to find:
When coming in the Dublin/Foxford Road, continue driving towards Ballina. Go straight through the first two sets of traffic lights. Go straight on at the roundabout. After about 1km, go right onto the narrow road. After approx. 1 minute you will see a sign for Belleek Castle on your left-hand side.

GPS coordinates
N54° 07 59.1 W-009° 08 42.5
N54.13307 W-9.14513

BISHOP'S GATE HOTEL

Perfectly positioned within the historic city walls, nestled in the heart of the "Cathedral Quarter" this iconic landmark is the epitome of Edwardian elegance; an intimate urban oasis featuring 30 luxurious guestrooms, including 2 suites, a resident's lounge, fitness area, restaurant and champagne bar. Bishop's Gate Hotel blends stunning Edwardian architecture, stylish appointments and luxurious facilities which have been sensitively restored to pay homage to the rich heritage of the building, whilst exceeding the contemporary needs and desires of its guests.

The way in which guests are welcomed, attended to during their stay and remembered when they come back is the essence of Bishop's Gate Hotel.

Georgina Campbells Hideaway of the Year 2017.
TripAdvisor Travellers Choice Awards 2017– Placed 2nd in the top 25 hotels, United Kingdom. **TripAdvisor** Travellers Choice Awards 2018 – Placed 3rd in the top 25 hotels, United Kingdom.
AA 1 Rosette for Culinary Excellence 2018.

Bedrooms **30**   Hotel ★ ★ ★ ★

Bishop's Gate Hotel
24a Bishop's Street, Derry, BT486PP
T +44 (0)28 711 40300
sales@bishopsgatehotelderry.com
www.bishopsgatehotelderry.com

Proprietors: Ciaran and Ann Marie O'Neill
Rates From £129 Bed and Breakfast.

How to find:
1 Hour 15 Minutes from Belfast International Airport Via A6.
3 Hours From Dublin Airport Via A5.
Nestled where the Wild Atlantic Way meets The Causeway Coastal Route.

GPS coordinates
54.994772
-7.323118

BLAIRSCOVE HOUSE RESTAURANT AND ACCOMMODATION

In this Georgian country house standing at the head of Dunmanus Bay, everything revolves around the courtyard. Finely restored with cobbled paths, shrubs and flowers, it's 500 year old stone outbuildings contain four beautiful apartments as well as the restaurant with its magnificent dining room.

Blairscove Restaurant is best known for its buffet style starters and scrumptious desserts.

The elegant setting, the pretty courtyard and the landscaped gardens make it an ideal venue for weddings of up to 100 guests.

AA 2 rosettes for culinary excellence 2018
AA **** for Accommodation 2018
One Fab Day 100 best wedding venues 2018
TripAdvisor Certificate of Excellence 2018
Michelin Guide 2018
McKennas Guides 100 Best Places to Stay 2018

Bedrooms **4 courtyard suites, self catering also available**

**Blairscove House & Restaurant,
Durrus, Bantry, Co.Cork, P75 FE44**
T +353 (0)27 61127
mail@blairscove.ie
www.blairscove.ie

**Proprietors: The De Mey Family
Restaurant**:
Open from March 14th – November 2nd 2019.
Tuesday- Saturday 6:00pm-9:30pm..
3 course table d'hôte menu €60.
Accommodation:
Open from March 14th – November 3rd 2019.
Bed & Breakfast from €150 – €260 per room
B&B midweek
Friday & Saturday €220 – €260 per room B&B
Most major credit cards accepted, apart from
American Express.

How to find: Coming from Durrus, follow the
R591 to Crookhaven. After 2.5km you'll see the
blue gate on the right hand side.
Cork airport: 1hr 15mins.

GPS coordinates
51 degrees 36' 33" N
9 degrees 32' 18" W

BUSHMILLS INN HOTEL

Set against the backdrop of the Causeway Coast, the boutique Bushmills Inn Hotel and Restaurant offers the perfect base to explore the Giant's Causeway, Carrick-a-Rede Rope Bridge, Bushmills Distillery, Dunluce Castle and many of the Game of Thrones filming locations.

Indulge in exquisite cuisine in our AA Rosette Restaurant, relax in our traditional Gas Bar with a glass of whiskey and then enjoy a restful night's sleep in a bedroom individually designed with unique character and charm.

From roaring peat fires and nooks and crannies just waiting to be explored, the Inn epitomises the true spirit of Irish hospitality.

Northern Ireland Tourism Awards Hotel of the Year 2015, 2017 & 2018
Northern Ireland Tourism Awards Customer Service Excellence 2016 & 2017
The Good Eating Guide Best Hotel Restaurant in Ulster 2018
Golfers Guide to Ireland Best Boutique Golf Hotel in Ireland 2017
TripAdvisor Travellers' Choice Awards top 25 UK Hotels 2016 & 2017

Bedrooms **41**   Specialist accommodation **Historic Building**   Hotel ★ ★ ★ ★

Bushmills Inn Hotel, 9 Dunluce Road, Bushmills, Co.Antrim, BT57 8QG
T + 44(0)28 207 33000
info@bushmillsinn.com
www.bushmillsinn.com

Proprietor: Alan Dunlop
Hotel Manager: Alan Walls
Open all year Monday to Sunday.
Restaurant open all day: 12 noon to 9.30,
dinner 6pm to 9.30pm Stg£30.
B&B: Low Season: Nov – Mar from £65 pps.
High Season: April – Oct from £110 pps.
All bedrooms non-smoking.
Credit Cards: Amex, Mastercard, Visa.

How to find:
From Belfast follow the M2 north to Ballymena then A26 to Ballymoney. At the roundabout take the third exit onto B62 heading to Portrush/Bushmills, turn right onto Priestland Road (B17) then right onto Dunluce Road (A2). The Bushmills Inn will be on the left.

GPS coordinates
N 55 12' 25.64"
W 6 31' 26.63"

Butler House & Garden is the charming Dower House of Kilkenny Castle since 1786. Nestled in the heart of vibrant medieval Kilkenny, Butler House brings history, charm, romance and a warm welcome to all who visit. Sleep, dine, or celebrate those milestones in life in timeless and unique surroundings.

Butler House boasts fourteen unique bedrooms and suites, all with their own individual character. Designed to provide maximum comfort, each has a modern bathroom, and is decorated with soft coordinated fabrics and furnishings.

Butler House kitchen ensures every dish is perfectly prepared and the ethos is that the best meals start with the best ingredients. Wherever possible we will source the finest local, natural, organic and seasonal ingredients, within a 60-km radius of the property.

Awards: Highly commended Irish Breakfast with **Georgina Campbell** 2018.

Bedrooms **14**

Specialist accommodation **Historic Building**

Butler House
16 Patrick St, Kilkenny City, Ireland.
T +353 (0)56 7722828
res@butler.ie
www.butler.ie

Proprietors: Kilkenny Civic Trust
Closed 23rd December to 27th December.
Rates: Bed and Breakfast from €139 per night.

How to find:
Kilkenny city centre, approx 70 mins from Dublin Airport on M9 and 120mins from Cork.

GPS coordinates
52.6489246 Lat
-7.250782 Long

CAHERNANE HOUSE HOTEL

Cahernane House Hotel is a unique experience of old Irish history mixed with modern luxuries. Beautifully situated on its own private estate on the edge of Killarney National Park and only a twenty minute walk to Killarney town centre.

Cahernane House Hotel exudes a sense of relaxation and peacefulness where guests can retreat from the hectic pace of life into a cocoon of calmness and serenity.

Dine on local produce in the award winning Herbert Restaurant or soak up the atmosphere in The Cellar, where you can enjoy a drink or a casual dining experience from our all day dining menu.

Awards include: **AA** 2 Rosettes for Culinary Excellence.

Listed as part of the **Conde Nast** Johansens collection of luxury travel destinations, a worldwide reference guide for exceptional places to stay.

Bedrooms **40** (12 of which are in the Manor House)   Hotel ★ ★ ★ ★

Cahernane House Hotel
Muckross Road, Cahernane, Killarney
Co. Kerry, Ireland, V93 E78W
T +353 64 663 1895
info@cahernane.com
www.cahernane.com

Proprietors: Prem Group Ltd.
General Manager: Emer Corridan
Bed & Breakfast from €160 per room per night
Closed midweek in November & December.
Open for Christmas and New Year 2018.
Open from March 8th 2019.
Herbert Restaurant open Saturday to Friday nights
from 6.30pm – 9pm.
Cellar Bar Menu daily from 1pm – 9.30pm.

How to find:
4 hours drive from Dublin.
25 minutes drive from Kerry Airport.
From Killarney town, take the N72 south. Hotel is located on the right after crossing the Flesk River.

GPS coordinates
Lat: 52.043169
Long: -9.509847

GDS Codes:
Amadeus – YX KIRCHH
Sabre – YX 321693
Galileo/Apollo – YX E7454
Worldspan – YX ORKCH
Pep ADS / Travelhub
– YX 4168

CAMPAGNE RESTAURANT

Campagne, a Michelin starred restaurant located in the heart of medieval Kilkenny. Established in 2008, the emphasis has been to serve food based on high quality seasonal produce with French influences.

Located under the old railway arches on Gas House lane, Campagne boasts a stylish interior featuring oak flooring, curved banquette seating and modern paintings depicting rural life by local artist Catherine Barron.

Campagne has been awarded many prestigious awards on a national and international level, most notably one Michelin star in September 2013.

Campagne Restaurant
5 The Arches, Gas House Lane,
Kilkenny, R95 X092
T +353 (0)56 777 2858
info@campagne.ie
www.campagne.ie

Proprietors: Garrett Byrne & Brid Hannon
Opening hours:
Lunch; Friday, Saturday & Sunday 12.30pm-2.30pm
Early Bird Dinner; Wednesday & Thursday 6 – 7pm,
Friday 5.30 – 7pm, Saturday 5 – 6pm
A la carte Dinner; Wednesday to Saturday 6 – 10pm
Open Sunday nights on bank holiday weekends
Closed Mondays & Tuesdays
Annual Holidays; 2 weeks in January, 1 week
in July

How to find:
Campagne is located just under the cities old
railway arches, in an area called John's green,
the restaurant is in close proximity to Mc Donagh
Junction shopping centre.

GPS coordinates
52"8304;39'21" N
7"8304;14'47" W

CARRIG COUNTRY HOUSE

Hidden away on the shores of Caragh Lake, Ring of Kerry, enchanting 'Carrig' offers an 'escape from it all' and the most beautiful scenery in Ireland.

Enjoy golf, fishing, horse riding or hiking. Tour the Ring of Kerry, Dingle Peninsula, Killarney National Park or World Heritage Site Skellig Michael.

Snuggle up in a comfy king size bed and awake to the sound of the lake lapping on the shore. Stroll the wonderful gardens or indulge in a good book or game of chess in the spacious Drawing Rooms.

Savour fine wines and mouth-watering Irish Country House cooking in our award winning **Lakeside Restaurant**. Frank, Mary, Claire and Team extend a warm welcome and unique Irish Country House experience.

Gold Medal Awards "Ireland's Country House 2015/16."
Irish Restaurant Awards Best Chef in Kerry 2015.
Georgina Campbell's Ireland Guide "Country House of the Year 2013."
FODOR's International Guide – "Fodor's Choice."
2 AA Rosettes for Culinary Excellence.

Bedrooms **17** (including 2 Suites)   Country House ★ ★ ★ ★

Carrig Country House & Restaurant,
Caragh Lake, Killorglin, Co.Kerry V93 WK83
T +353 (0)66 976 9100
info@carrighouse.com www.carrighouse.com

Hosts / Proprietors: Frank & Mary Slattery
Closed November – February inclusive.
Bed & breakfast per person sharing:
€75 – €155 pps Low Season.
€95 – €195 pps High Season.
Single supplement €60 – €75.
2 & 3 Day Value Package price on
www.carrighouse.com
Dinner: A La Carte or Dinner Menu available from
6.30-9pm.
Visa, Mastercard, Maestro Accepted.
Children over the age of 8 years are welcome.

How to find:
From Killorglin (10 minutes) – N70 from Killorglin towards Glenbeigh for 4km. After PROMED offices, take 2nd left for Caragh Lake (signposted). At Caragh Lake School and Shop see signpost for Carrig, take sharp right, located 1km further on the left.
From Glenbeigh (10 minutes) – Take the N70 in the direction of Killorglin for 4km, go over one-way stone bridge turning right, continue for approx. 1km and turn right onto the Caragh Lake road (Carrig signpost, before the Red Fox Inn) and drive for 2km. Carrig Country House is on the right.

GPS coordinates
N 52 4' 26.23"
W 9 51' 0.58"

CASHEL HOUSE HOTEL COUNTRY HOUSE & RESTAURANT

A perfect start on the Wild Atlantic Way – Cashel House Hotel is a cosy 18th Century Historic House, in 50 acres of magnificent gardens on the beautiful coastline of Cashel Bay with Cashel Hill rising behind.

Owned by the McEvilly family for 50 years, a warm welcome awaits. You can unwind and enjoy a quiet peaceful atmosphere. Relax in our Drawing Rooms with open fires & antiques. Retire to comfortable Romantic Double or spacious Mini Suite. Dine in our restaurant overlooking the gardens and simple Country House Cuisine. Local Seafood and Connemara Lamb Dishes, all served with vegetables from our garden.

Enjoy walking, beaches, sea and lake fishing, riding, hiking, golf, visit Kylemore Abbey, Aran or Inish Boffin Island or a boat trip around Killary Fjord.

Awards: **AA** Inspector Choice Award, **AA** 2 Rosettes & included in 1000 places to see before you die.

Bedrooms **28**   Hotel ★ ★ ★ ★

**Cashel House Hotel, Cashel,
Connemara, Co.Galway, H91 XE10**
T +353 (0)95 31001
sales@cashelhouse.ie
www.cashelhouse.ie

Proprietors: The McEvilly Family
Closed January and reopen on 11 February.
Bed & Breakfast from €75 – €95 per person sharing
Suites from €125 – €150 per person sharing
Children welcome.
Special Breaks on request.
Dinner: 3 course €38.00, 5 course €55.00,
A la Carte also available.
All major credit cards accepted.
Pet friendly.

Exclusive wedding parties 120 max.
Gratuity at your discretion.

How to find:
South off N59 (Galway Clifden Road).
1.6 kilometres (1 mile) west of Recess, turn left.

GPS coordinates
53.419547
-9.807950

CASTLE DURROW

One of Ireland's luxurious Country House Hotels, Castle Durrow was built in 1716 by William Flower on the banks of the river Erkina. The Castle has been lovingly restored by Peter & Shelly in a comfortable, relaxing and contemporary style.

Explore the estate with herbaceous borders, a walled garden, where lots of produce is grown for our award winning restaurant and the surrounding woodlands and riverbanks.

There are two dining options at the Castle, the elegant main restaurant and the more casual grillroom conservatory.

We are one of Ireland's most popular Castle wedding venues.

TripAdvisor – 2016 top 10 castle hotels in the WORLD, 2017 top 10 of Irish hotels, 2017 No 4 luxury hotel in Ireland.
Irish Restaurant Association Awards Winner – 2010 up to and including 2017.
One Fab Day – Top 100 Wedding Venues in Ireland.

Bedrooms **46 and quirky Gate Lodge**

Castle Durrow,
Durrow, Co.Laois, R32EA02
T +353 (0)57 873 6555
F +353 (0)57 873 6559
info@castledurrow.com
www.castledurrow.com
Facebook @CastleDurrow

Proprietors: The Stokes Family
Open all year but closed for Christmas
24–26 December inc.
Restaurant open: Thursday to Sunday.
Grillroom open: Wednesday to Sunday.
Dinner, Bed & Breakfast from €240 per couple.
Four course dinner from €42pp.
Sunday lunch from €32.50pp.
Afternoon Tea from €23pp.

Private Dining Rooms available for special occasions.

How to find:
From Dublin: On M7 take exit 17 then N77 through Abbeyleix to Durrow.
From Cork: On M8 take exit 4 then R639 through Johnstown, Cullohill to Durrow.

GPS Coordinates:
Lat: 52.846301
Long: -7.401223

CASTLE GROVE

Castle Grove is a family-run Georgian house, built in 1695 and set in its own 250-acre estate with gardens designed by "Capability" Brown. Situated at the end of a mile-long avenue on the shores of Lough Swilly it's the perfect base to explore beautiful Donegal and Wild Atlantic way.

Two drawing rooms with open fireplaces, library, cosy bar and bedrooms are furnished with antiques and luxury fabrics.

The award-winning fine dining restaurant serves excellent cuisine prepared by our Master Chefs, who combine locally sourced produce with organically grown fruit and vegetables from the four acre Walled Garden.

Ideal for weddings, and special occasions; Castle Grove is described as *"a hidden gem in Donegal."*

2018 Top 25 Small Hotels of Ireland **(Trip Advisor)**.
2017, 2016, 2015, 2014, 2013, 2012, 2011 – Hall of Fame Excellence Award **(TripAdvisor)**.

Bedrooms **15**   Hotel ★ ★ ★ ★

Castle Grove House
Letterkenny, Co. Donegal, F92 A462
T +353 (0)74 91 51118
stay@castlegrove.com
www.castlegrove.com
@castlegrove1695 – Facebook

Proprietors: The Sweeney Family
Open all year round, except Christmas.
Low Season: €110 – €200
High Season: €150 – €250
Dinner: A' la carte and €38 prix fix
Sunday Lunch: €27
Afternoon Tea: 12 to 5pm daily
Customized Menu's and cakes available.

How to find:
From Dublin: Take the M1, then N2 and onto the A5 via Omagh. Follow signs to Letterkenny (N14). From Belfast take the M2/M22, then the A6, and follow signs to Letterkenny.
From Letterkenny follow signs to Ramelton (R245) for 2.8 Miles. Turn right at the junction and follow the signs to Castle Grove Country House Hotel.
City of Derry and Donegal airports 45 mins (collection service available).

GPS Coordinates:
Latitude: 54.986436
Longitude: -7.660938

CASTLE LESLIE ESTATE

Nestled on 1,000 acres of undulating Irish countryside, dotted with ancient woodland and glittering lakes, Castle Leslie Estate is one of the last great Irish castle estates still in the hands of its founding family.

The Castle offers authentic original interiors and old-style hospitality.

The Lodge is a country house style boutique hotel with 2 AA Rosette award winning Snaffles Restaurant. Explore the Estate on horseback and enjoy some of the many other activities on offer including clay target shooting, archery, fishing, walking trails, the spa, hot air balloon rides, falconry or horse drawn carriage rides.

Hotel and Catering Review Gold Medal Award 2017: Ireland's Favourite Place to Stay.
Condé Nast Johansens 2018 Excellence Award: Best for Weddings, Parties and Special Occasions.
Luxury Travel Guide Global Awards 2018: Luxury Castle Hotel of the Year.

Bedrooms **49**

Specialist accommodation **Historic Castle**

Castle Leslie Estate, Glaslough, Co.Monaghan
T +353 (0)47 88100
info@castleleslie.com
www.castleleslie.com

Proprietor: Sammy Leslie
CEO: Brian Baldwin
Bed and Breakfast:
From €95pps at The Lodge.
From €115pps at The Castle.

Single occupancy (Bed and Breakfast)
From €170 at The Lodge.
From €210 at The Castle.

How to find:
From Dublin take M1 north. Exit at Junction 14 for Ardee. Follow N2 Monaghan/Derry. Continue on the N2 to Monaghan bypass – do not enter town. 1st roundabout follow N2 for Derry. Continue to 3rd roundabout. Take 3rd exit signposted Armagh (N12). Follow N12 for 2 miles. Turn left at signpost for Glaslough (R185). Follow road to Glaslough. 80 minutes from Dublin, 60 minutes from Belfast.

GPS coordinates
Lat: 54.31821
Long: -6.89582

Garmin Loc8 code
G6E-22-5TK

Chapter One Restaurant is located in Dublin city centre on the north side of Parnell Square. As a former home of John Jameson, it retains authentic granite walls and sash windows and has been carefully and stylishly renovated to create a wonderfully sumptuous and comfortable restaurant.

It is one of Dublin's leading restaurants having won numerous awards for both food and service. The front of house team are warm and friendly while retaining a high level of efficiency and professionalism.

It is Dublin's premier pre-theatre dining venue. Chapter One proprietor, Ross Lewis has continued to strive for excellence and this effort is manifest throughout the restaurant. A rare treat awaits you.

Chapter One Restaurant
18/19 Parnell Square, Dublin
T +353 (0)1 873 2266
F +353 (0)1 873 2330
info@chapteronerestaurant.com
www.chapteronerestaurant.com

Proprietor: Ross Lewis
Opening hours:
Closed Sunday & Monday
Pre Theatre Dinner: Tuesday to Saturday 5pm–7.30pm
Dinner Sitting: Tuesday to Saturday 7.30pm–10.30pm
Lunch: Friday 12.30pm – 2.00pm
Annual Holidays: Christmas – two weeks;
August – two weeks.

Private Dining: The Jameson Room: 14 people.
The Vault Room: 16 people.

How to find:
Centre of Dublin – Parnell Square
is at the top of O'Connell Street.

CLARE ISLAND LIGHTHOUSE

This 200 year old lighthouse, situated on Clare Island in Clew Bay County Mayo, has been completely restored and opened for guests in 2013. Its location high on the cliffs, 120 meters above the sea, enables spectacular views over the Atlantic Ocean and surrounding areas.

Our interiors, in keeping with the ethos of the Lighthouse, are understated but exceedingly comfortable.

The eclectic heritage Lighthouse offers "wholesome" food based on local produce complimented by a good selection of international wines.

There is lots to do… Walking, swimming, hiking, cycling, birdwatching, reading or simply relaxing beside a turf fire.

Clare Island Lighthouse is one of the GREAT LIGHTHOUSES of Ireland on the Wild Atlantic Way.

World Boutique Hotel Award Best Coastal Boutique Hotel in Europe WINNER 2016.
Trip Advisor – Certificate of Excellence.

Accommodation **5 bedrooms/Suites**   Specialist accommodation **Lighthouse**

Clare Island Lighthouse
T +353 (0)87 668 9758
info@clareislandlighthouse.com
bookinglighthouse@gmail.com
www.clareislandlighthouse.com

Proprietor: The Fischer Family
General Manager: Ms Roie Mc Cann
April 17th (Easter) - September 29th 2019.
Children over 16.
€250 - €300 pps for 1 night
Includes BB and Dinner.
Single supplement €250/ €300.
Visa and MasterCard accepted.
Doggies on request

How to find:
Directions from Westport to Clare Island –
Take the R335 to Louisburgh (20km).
Approximately 1.5km after Louisburgh town take
a right turn for Roonagh Pier (approx 7km).
The ferry sails from Roonagh Pier to Clare Island.
(20 minutes approx.).

GPS coordinates
53.82822 N
-9.98340 E

2 hours from Dublin in the dramatic North West, a genuine, romantic, Grand Irish Country House with comfort, character and great home grown food.

A stunning mile long avenue crossing the River Unshin and winding through ancient woods and deer pastures on the 500 acre Private Estate brings you to this fabulous Georgian mansion. Warm hospitality, original antiques, spacious bedrooms and views from every window create an oasis of peace, quiet and relaxation.

Located by the Wild Atlantic Way it's the perfect base for exploring WB Yeats country, Lissadell House, links golf, hiking around lakes, mountains & neolithic tombs and surfing & horse riding on empty beaches.

Recent Accolades:
John & Sally McKenna's 100 Best Places to Stay 2018.
Sunday Telegraph Best 3 Irish Country House Hotels.
Restaurant Association Best Hotel Restaurant Sligo.
Conde Nast Traveller Ireland's 5 Best Country House Hotels.

Bedrooms **8**   Specialist accommodation **Historic House**

Coopershill House, Riverstown, Co.Sligo, F52 EC52
T +353 (0)71 916 5108
ohara@coopershill.com
www.coopershill.com

Proprietor: The O'Hara Family
Open April to end of October.
Open all year for house parties.
Bed & Breakfast.
from €202 – €250 per room.
Special offers for 2+ nights
4 course dinner at 8.00pm €56 p/p.

How to find:
On N4 route to Dublin 19km south-east of Sligo. At crossroads follow signs to Riverstown and Coopershill.

GPS coordinates
N 54.1381
W 8.4154

CURRAREVAGH HOUSE

Old fashioned (in the best sense of the word), Currarevagh is situated on the shores of Lough Corrib in 150 acres of private woodland estate, now a European Special Area of Conservation. It is run as a private country house rather than a hotel, and the tranquil informality lends itself to those seeking to escape today's hectic world.

Built by the present owner's ancestors in 1842, the exceptional food, cooked by Lucy with flair, originality and passion, and magical grounds take centre stage. Having Connemara and the Aran Islands within easy touring reach, our own boats for guests use, many walks and abundant wildlife – it all makes a unique, original and wonderful experience not to be missed.

Tripadvisor Traveller's Choice 2018 Top 10 Small Hotels in Ireland.

Recommended by Georgina Campbell, Good Hotel Guide, Michelin Guide and others.
Sunday Telegraph Review – 9/10 (Fiona Duncan).

Bedrooms **12**   Specialist accommodation **Historic House ★ ★ ★ ★**

Currarevagh House, Oughterard, Connemara, Co.Galway
T +353 (0)91 552312
rooms@currarevagh.com
www.currarevagh.com

Proprietors: The Hodgson Family
Open March 1st to November 30th 2019.
Bed and Breakfast from €70.00 – €90.00 pps.
Single Rooms available.
Dinner €50.00.

How to find:
Take the N59 (Galway/Clifden) road to Oughterard. Turn right in village square and follow the Glann road for 6kms.

Extra information:
Reduced Half Board Rates for visits of 2 or more days. Weekly half board rate from €820 pp per week.
Out of season house parties are welcome (excluding Christmas and New Year).

GPS coordinates
N 53 27.657
W 9 21.518

DUNBRODY HOUSE

COUNTRY HOUSE HOTEL & SPA

Indulgence is the order of the day at Dunbrody Country House with gourmet restaurant, chic champagne seafood bar and leisurely breakfasts.
Couple this foodie focus with our aim to please and you'll understand Dunbrody's desirability.

In 300 acres of parkland on the idyllic Hook Peninsula on Ireland's south coast, 1830s Dunbrody is the perfect year-round getaway to the country.   Relaxed elegance & country house chic with individually-styled rooms, very much in keeping with the hotel's Georgian origins and late breakfast til Noon make it easy to avail of long, lazy lie-ins…

For the culinary inquisitives there's the cookery school temptation with choice of 1, 2 & 5 day courses and for those seeking some me-time why not indulge in our luxury boutique Spa.

"The Local" – our traditional pub entices too with great gastro-pub menu and live music. For the ultimate hideaway, try our new woodland retreat – the Cosy Cabin.

Bedrooms **22** including Suites and Guest Lodge   Hotel ★ ★ ★ ★

Dunbrody Country House Hotel, Arthurstown, Y34 R597 Co. Wexford
T +353 (0)51 389600
F +353 (0)51 389601
info@dunbrodyhouse.com
www.dunbrodyhouse.com

Proprietors: Catherine & Kevin Dundon
B&B from €75 – €155 pps low season,
€95 – €195 pps high season.
Single Supplement €25 per night on
standard double rooms.
Seasonal 5 course Dinner Menu €65 and
€80 8 course Tasting Menu.

How to find:
M11/N11 from south Dublin and then the
R733 to Arthurstown.
M9 from north Dublin to New Ross and then the
R733 to Arthurstown.
N25 from Cork/Waterford and the Passage East
car ferry to Ballyhack.

ENNISCOE HOUSE

Hidden among the woods at the foot of Nephin is Enniscoe, 'the last Great House of North Mayo' overlooking the waters of Lough Conn. The estate has been in the family since the 1650's and the classical Georgian house dates from the 1790's.

The current generation, Susan Kellett and her son Dj, are happy to share their house and grounds with guests. There are elegant reception rooms and fine bedrooms with stunning views over lake and park. Outside are pastures, shrubberies, miles of woodland and lakeside walks, a carefully restored Victorian pleasure garden and an organic vegetable garden. Good food, freshly prepared, uses fruit and vegetables from the garden as well as other local produce.

Good Hotel Guide Editor's Choice Award Fishing 2017.
Recommended by Alistair Sawday, Georgina Campbell, Good Hotel Guide, Michelin Guide and others.
Where delicious things begin. Catherine Cleary, Irish Times.

Bedrooms **6**   Specialist accommodation **Historic House**

Enniscoe House, Castlehill, Ballina, Co.Mayo, F26EA34
T +353 (0)96 31112
mail@enniscoe.com
www.enniscoe.com

Proprietor: Susan Kellett and Dj Kellett
Open 1st April to 31st October
Bed & Breakfast from €90 – €130 pps.
Dinner €50 at 7.30 / 8.00pm.
Single supplement €30.
Dogs welcome.

How to find:
Enniscoe is 3.2km south of the village of Crossmolina on the R315 to Pontoon and Castlebar. It is 20km from Ballina.

Ireland West Airport Knock 50 km.

GPS coordinates
N Lat. 54075060
W. 9312633

Built in 1727, Ghan House is a listed Georgian House & Restaurant within 3 acres of walled mature gardens.

Just a tree length away from medieval Carlingford – with its narrow streets, town gate, castles, priory & ancient walls – a stone's throw from Carlingford Lough. 1 hour from Dublin & Belfast.

The 2 AA Rosette restaurant utilises the herb & vegetable gardens & celebrates its position;- on Carlingford Lough with the local seafood & mountain lamb/beef.

Whether you stay in the old house or the garden bedrooms, views of Carlingford Lough, the Mourne Mountains or Slieve Foy are standard. Mountain walks, Carlingford Greenway, Scenic Carlingford Ferry.

Awards: 2 **AA** Rosettes since 2011, **4* AA** accommodation.
John & Sally McKenna's "Best 100 Places to stay in Ireland" since 1999.
'Alastair Sawday' & 'Georgina Campbell' guides since 1999.
One Fab Day 'Best 100 Wedding Venues'.

Bedrooms **12**

Specialist accommodation **Historic House**

Ghan House, Carlingford, Co.Louth
T +353 (0)42 937 3682
info@ghanhouse.com
www.ghanhouse.com

Proprietor: Paul & Joyce Carroll
Open all year.
(Closed 24 – 26th, 31st December & 1st
& 2nd January).
B&B from €85 pps – €125 pps.
4 course dinner €50.00, most nights
6pm – 9.30pm.
6 course midweek tasting menu €42.50
6pm to 7.45pm.
Special midweek & weekend dinner &
B&B breaks.
All major credit cards accepted.

No service charge. Gratuities at discretion of guests.

How to find:
Take junction 18 on main Dublin to Belfast M1 to Carlingford. On the left, 10 metres after 50kph sign on entrance to Carlingford is a stone entrance & gravel drive to Ghan House.

GPS coordinates
N54°02.373' W006°11.044' /
54.04028, - 6.18417

GLENLO ABBEY HOTEL

Welcoming open log fires and a warm welcome await you at Glenlo Abbey Hotel. This luxury, five star hotel is nestled on a stunning 138 acre estate overlooking Lough Corrib near Galway City.

Dine aboard the award-winning Pullman Restaurant, set on two original Orient Express carriages, now a fine dining restaurant on the hotel grounds. The 18th Century Abbey is the perfect venue for banquets, occasions and intimate weddings.

Take time to relax in one of the many reception rooms or take in a movie in the private Abbey Movie Theatre.

There is a great array of fresh air activities including Golf, Fishing on Lough Corrib and Falconry to enhance a memorable experience.

Awards include:
AA: Two AA Rosettes for the Pullman Restaurant since 2016.
RAI Awards: Best Private Dining and Club Restaurant 2017.

Bedrooms **46** Suites **4**   Hotel ★ ★ ★ ★ ★

Glenlo Abbey Hotel
Bushypark, Galway, H91 XD8K
T +353 (0)91 519600
stay@glenloabbey.ie
www.glenloabbeyhotel.ie

How to find:
From Galway City, take the N59 towards Connemara. The hotel is located 2 miles/ 4 kms from the city centre. After passing Bushypark church the hotel entrance is on the right hand side of road.

Proprietors: John and Marie Lally
Bed and Breakfast from €199 per room, per night.

GPS coordinates
Lat: 53.300406
Long: -9.098559000000023

GREGANS CASTLE

With breath taking views across Galway Bay and idyllically situated overlooking the unique Burren landscape, this is the ultimate luxury and gourmet hideaway.

Simon and Freddie together with their staff manage this oasis of comfort and offer genuine Irish hospitality, award winning innovative cooking and elegant bedrooms free from the intrusion of televisions. Antiques, an eclectic art collection, open fires, candles, jugs of flowers and Shelley the cat add to the indulgently relaxing atmosphere.

Located on the Wild Atlantic Way and the Burren Food Trail. The ideal location from which to enjoy the Burren, the Cliffs of Moher, Walking, Cycling, Aran Islands, Horse Riding, Surfing, Sea Angling, Golf.

Awards include:
Good Hotel Guide Irish Hotel of the Year 2019, **Georgina Campbell's** Best Breakfast 2018, **AA** 3 Rosettes for culinary excellence 2018, **Green Hospitality** Silver Award 2018, **Food & Wine** Best for Romance 2017.

Bedrooms **21**   Hotel ★ ★ ★ ★

Gregans Castle Hotel, The Burren, Ballyvaughan, Co. Clare, H91 CF60
T +353 (0)65 7077005
stay@gregans.ie
www.gregans.ie

Proprietors: Simon Haden and Frederieke McMurray
General Manager: Ken Bergin
Bed & Breakfast from €245.00 per room per night for two persons sharing.
Dinner from €45.00 to €75.00.

Open from February 15th to November 30th inclusive.

How to find:
On N67, 5km south of Ballyvaughan village.
1 hour from Shannon Airport and 2½ hours from Dublin.

GPS coordinates
53 04 36 79 N
9 11 11 19 W

HAYFIELD MANOR

Nestled within secluded gardens, Cork's premier 5 star hotel, Hayfield Manor provides the charm of a country house within the vibrant city of Cork. Splendid rooms and suites are classically styled and individually decorated. Guests with a penchant for exquisite food should sample the local fare showcased in the gourmet restaurant, Orchids, and in the contemporary dining space, Perrotts Garden Bistro. A delightful white-glove Afternoon Tea is also served daily.

The Beautique Spa features Elemis Spa Therapy, with pool, Jacuzzi, sauna, steam room and resident's gym. The concierge will assist you to discover the unique attractions of Cork city and county.

Awards include:
Georgina Campbell's Ireland Hotel of the Year, **Fodor's** Choice Award, **AA** Irish Hotel of the Year, **AA** 2 Rosettes for Culinary Excellence, **RAC** Gold Ribbon Award for Excellence. **Tripadvisor** Traveller's Choice Award, **Conde Nast** Reader's Choice Award.

Bedrooms **88**   Hotel ★ ★ ★ ★ ★

Hayfield Manor, Perrott Avenue, College Road, T12 HT97, Cork City
T +353 (0)21 484 5900
F +353 (0)21 431 6839
enquiries@hayfieldmanor.ie
www.hayfieldmanor.ie

Proprietors: Joe and Margaret Scally
Manager: TJ Mulcahy
Open all year round.
Manor Rooms: €99 pps to €220 pps.
Superior and Deluxe Rooms also available.
Suites: €245 pps to €650 pps.
Perrotts Garden Bistro: A la Carte.
Orchids: 5 course Gourmet Menu – €69 per person.
Afternoon Tea: 1pm – 4.30pm.
Private dining available.

Service charge of 10% on 8 people or more.
All major credit cards accepted.
Wheelchair accessible rooms available.
Interconnecting Family rooms available.

How to find:
6 miles from Cork International Airport (ORK), 80 miles from Shannon International Airport (SNN). Hayfield Manor is located off College Road, opposite University College Cork.

GDS codes: Amadeus- LX ORKHMR,
Apollo/Galileo- LX 78441,
Sabre- LX 31327,
Worldspan- LX ORKHM

GPS coordinates
N 51.89102
W -8.48953

HUNTER'S HOTEL

COUNTRY HOUSE HOTEL & RESTAURANT

Ireland's oldest coaching inn, in the 5th generation of the same family. Its picturesque gardens along the banks of the river Vartry provide a delightful setting for a delicious lunch, afternoon tea or a drink.

An ideal base from which to visit Mount Usher Gardens, Powerscourt, Russborough, Killruddery and Glendalough in County Wicklow, 'The Garden of Ireland'.

There are fifteen 18-hole golf courses nearby, most notably Druid's Glen and the European. Horse riding and hill walking can be arranged. Conference facilities available. Hunter's is approx. 60 minutes drive from Dublin, 30 minutes from Dun Laoghaire and 90 minutes from Rosslare.

Bedrooms **16**

Specialist accommodation **Hotel & Restaurant**

Hunter's Hotel, Newrath Bridge, Rathnew, Co.Wicklow
T +353 (0)404 40106
Facebook @HuntersIreland
reception@hunters.ie
www.hunters.ie

Proprietor: Gelletlie Family
Closed 24, 25, 26 & 31 December.
Bed & Breakfast from €65 – €95 per person.
Dinner from €29.50 served 7.30pm to 8.45pm.
Lunch from €19.75 served 1.00pm to 2.30pm.
Sunday Lunch from €35.00 served from 12.45pm.
Afternoon Tea from €17.50 served from 4.00pm.
Private dining available.
No Service Charge.

How to find:
From Dublin: Take exit 15 for Ashford off the N11. Turn left at the bridge in Ashford. Then 2km.
From Wexford/Rosslare: Take exit 16 for Ashford off the N11. Pass Mount Usher Gardens. Turn right at bridge in Ashford. Then 2km.

GPS coordinates
N 53.006374
W -6.084328

The Ice House is a wonderful fusion of old and new. Rooms and suites with panoramic views of the river Moy marry the original 18th century building with contemporary styling. With quirky details, fabulous fresh and local food and the riverside thermal garden, you have arrived somewhere very special indeed.

On the Wild Atlantic Way, close to Ireland West Airport, here's the perfect base for exploring the stunning coastline of the North West.

Irish Tatler Highly Commended Spa 2017.
Irish Times 100 Best Places to Stay 2017.
Irish Hair & Beauty Awards Best Spa 2016.

'Located on the Wild Atlantic Way, overlooking the River Moy and the woodlands beyond, the Ice House, Mayo is truly a one of a kind place,' Irish Tatler.

"Swish, small & delightfully situated. An excellent boutique hotel that offers an experience that is second to none,' Neil Hegarty, The Telegraph.

Bedrooms **32**   Hotel ★ ★ ★ ★

The Ice House, The Quay, Ballina, Co.Mayo
T +353 (0)96 23500
chill@theicehouse.ie
www.theicehouse.ie

Proprietor: Pearse Farrell
Open all year round.
(Closed 23 – 26 December).
Low season from €60pps B&B.
High season from €120pps..
Dinner served 6pm to 9pm, €45.
Bar Menu served 1pm to 9pm.
Sunday Lunch 1pm to 3pm, €27.
Afternoon Tea from €18 pp.
Children welcome.

How to find:
From Dublin – Follow N4/M4 route direction Sligo. At Longford follow N5 route direction Westport. Turn right onto N26 outside Swinford going through Foxford on to Ballina. On arrival in Ballina, follow N59 direction Sligo through the town and across the river. Turn left at traffic lights onto Quay Road. The Ice House is located ca. 1km on The Quay.

KILLARNEY ROYAL

Killarney town's most charming and central boutique hotel. For three generations, our family has held the mantle of caring for guests at the 4 star Killarney Royal, where visitors have been welcomed for over 100 years. Committed to delivering gracious hospitality and creating outstanding memories, we and our wonderful team deliver friendly personal service and true Irish hospitality.

We provide luxurious accommodation, exceptional and innovative cuisine and, with our town centre location, the ideal abode from which to explore the bustling town of Killarney. Our door is always open and we look forward to welcoming you very soon.

Awards include:
IGTOA Boutique Golf Hotel of the Year Award.
TripAdvisor Travellers Choice.

Bedrooms **32**

Hotel ★ ★ ★ ★

**Killarney Royal, College Street,
Killarney Town, V93 XC90, Co. Kerry**
T +353 (0)64 6631853
F +353 (0)64 6634001
reception@killarneyroyal.ie
www.killarneyroyal.ie

**Proprietors: Joe and Margaret Scally
Manager: Kamile Ambrozaite**
Closed 24, 25, 26 December.
Royal Rooms: €49.50 pps to €160.00 pps.
Deluxe and Junior Suites also available.
Suites: €74.50 pps to €180.00 pps.
The Royal Bar & Bistro: A la Carte.
The Candle Room Restaurant: €32.00 per person.
Afternoon Tea for Two: €35.00
Private dining available.
Service charge of 10% on 8 people or more.

All major cards accepted.
Free town centre parking.

How to find:
140 meters from Killarney train station
11mi /17km From Kerry International Airport
54mi /87km From Cork International Airport
84mi /135kms From Shannon International Airport
GDS Codes: Amadeus: LM KIR170,
Galileo/Apollo: LM 38135,
Sabre: LM 060601,
WorldSpan: LM 08170

GPS coordinates
N 52.059787
W -9.506131

KING SITRIC

Located in the picturesque fishing village of Howth, established in 1971, the MacManus family has built an international reputation for warm hospitality along with fresh local seafood. Panoramic sea views, the lapping of the water, the sounds of the sea birds... only 20 minutes from Dublin Airport and 25 minutes by DART into Dublin City.

Lobster, Crab and Shrimp are caught by our local fishermen in Balscadden Bay, only metres from the restaurant and our fish is landed daily on Howth Pier. East Café Bar is open all day, with seating on the terrace.

Walking, golfing, sailing, paddle boarding, diving….Lots to do. Stay a few days!

Awards:

Food & Wine – Hall of Fame: Aidan & Joan Mac Manus.
National Hospitality Awards – overall winner Best Seafood Restaurant 2014.
Hot Press Best of Dublin 2017.
Georgina Campbell Irish Breakfast Awards 2017 – Irish Bread Award – King Sitric Brown Bread.

Bedrooms **8**   Guesthouse ★ ★ ★ ★

**King Sitric, Fish Restaurant
& Accommodation, East Pier,
Howth, Co.Dublin D13 F5C6**
T +353 (0)1 832 5235
reservations@kingsitric.ie
www.kingsitric.ie

Proprietors: The MacManus Family
Bed & Breakfast from €155 per room.
Special short breaks available.
Babies and children welcome – under 12s sharing
with parents free.
Small dogs by arrangement.
Dinner Wednesday – Saturday from 6.00pm.
Sundays 1.00pm – 4.00pm.
East Café Bar open every day from 10.30am.
Private Dining, Weddings, Meetings, etc.
Closed last 2 weeks Jan.

How to find:
Coming in to Howth, all the way across the
harbour front to the end of the road, top of the
far pier.

GPS coordinates
Latitude 53.23 18 N
Longitude 06.03 48 W

Michelin Starred l'Ecrivain Restaurant is located in the heart of Georgian Dublin since 1989. This modern contemporary multi Award winning restaurant is run by Chef Derry Clarke, his wife Sallyanne & a dedicated professional Restaurant & Kitchen Team.

As well as a beautifully appointed dining room, and covered roof terrace, there are three Private Rooms: The Malt Room, seats 12; Our Chef's Kitchen – Private Room with a 'live' kitchen where our team of chefs cook in front of guests seats 20 plus: The Salon Privee seats 20 people.

We cater for Corporate Events, Weddings and Private Parties.

Awards:
Best Chef Ireland 2015 & 2016 **Good Eating Guide.**
Best Chef Dublin 2015 **Food & Wine Magazine.**
Best Business Restaurant 2017 **Food & Wine Magazine.**

l'Ecrivain Restaurant
109a Lower Baggot Street, Dublin 2
T +353 (0)1 661 1919
F +353 (0)1 661 0617
enquiries@lecrivain.com
www.lecrivain.com
Facebook @lEcrivain.Restaurant
Twitter @lEcrivainDublin
Instagram @lecrivaindublin

Proprietors: Derry and Sallyanne Clarke
Extensive Wine List and Cocktail List available.
Main Restaurant seats 90.
The Malt Room – Private Dining Room seats 12.
Salon Privè – Private Dining Room seats 20.
Chef's Kitchen seats 20.

Lunch: Friday 12.30pm to 2.00pm. Monday – Friday for December.
Dinner: Monday to Saturday 6.30pm to 10.30pm.
Reservations recommended.

How to find:
Under the Archway on Lower Baggot Street, right beside Lad Lane and only 5 mins walk from St. Stephen's Green, Merrion Square and Fitzwilliam Square.

LISS ARD ESTATE

The 163-acre Estate offers stylish accommodation which blends contemporary design with old world charm from the 19th Century Georgian Country House with adjacent Garden Mews to the Victorian Lake Lodge.

A magically timeless place, Liss Ard offers an ideal escape for those seeking a little time out. From the natural environment of its extensive gardens containing the unique James Turrell "Irish Sky Garden" to the quiet solitude of its private lake, Liss Ard will remain in your thoughts long after you depart – perfect for a getaway or holding your dream wedding.

Our culinary team offers you exquisite food in a modern Irish style presenting fresh, clean flavours complementing the many local food artisans of West Cork.

Awards include: **One Fab Day** Top 51 Exclusive Wedding Venues in Ireland.
Trip Advisor Certificate of excellence 2014-2017.
Michelin Guide 2017. 2 AA Rosettes for the Restaurant.
AA 5-star guest accommodation for the Country House.

Bedrooms/Suites **25**   Luxury Country House & Estate

Liss Ard Estate, Castletownshend Road, Skibbereen, Co.Cork
T:+353 (0)28 40000
F:+353 (0)28 40001
reservations@lissard.com
www.lissardestate.com

Rooms from €50pps – €150pps.
À la carte Dinner, 3 course from €35pp.
Open all year for weddings, groups and special events.

How to find:
Liss Ard is two minutes from Skibbereen town centre. From Cork Airport, follow the N71 to West Cork & Skibbereen. At Skibbereen follow the one way system to the Regal Roundabout with the VW dealership. Take the first exit and follow the signs to Castletownshend, A596. The entrance to the Liss Ard Estate is less than 1 kilometre on the right-hand-side.

GPS coordinates
51.532348250305326
(Latitude)
-9.249801635742188
(Longitude)

LONGUEVILLE HOUSE COUNTRY HOUSE & RESTAURANT

Nestled in 450 acres of wooded estate, Longueville House (c1720) a romantic Georgian Heritage Mansion is owned and run by the O'Callaghan family, your hosts. An ideal location for romantic breaks, exclusive use residential weddings & house parties, corporate events and family occasions. Longueville offers on-site private salmon & brown trout fly fishing on the River Blackwater, Falconry and seasonal events – May Dawn Chorus Walks, Autumn Mushroom Hunts, and pre-Christmas pop up shops to name a few. Both artisan beverages LH Brandy & LH Cider are made on site. Our Restaurant, with a field to fork policy offers the freshest produce from our gardens & farm with kitchen supervised by internationally commended chef/patron William O'Callaghan.

One Fab Day 100 Best Wedding Venues 2013 – 2017.
Trip Advisor Certificate of Excellence 2017.
Irish Food Awards for Longueville Apple Brandy.

Bedrooms **20**   Listed Heritage Property ★ ★ ★ ★

Longueville House and Restaurant, Mallow, Co.Cork
T +353 (0)22 47156
F +353 (0)22 47459
info@longuevillehouse.ie
www.longuevillehouse.ie

Proprietor: The O'Callaghan Family
Opening Hours: Open year round, Wednesday to Sunday.
Will open for groups in excess of 20 Guests Mon/Tues by prior arrangement.
Winter opening hours more limited, please consult hotel website.

How to find:
West of Mallow via the N72 road to Killarney, take the second Ballyclough junction on Right-hand side (approx. 3.3 miles via N72 from Mallow roundabout). Hotel entrance is 100 yards on left-hand side.

GPS coordinates
N52° 08. 308
W008° 44. 188

MARLFIELD HOUSE

Marlfield House is set on 36 acres of grounds, just outside Gorey, one hour south of Dublin. A very romantic country house, Marlfield has 19 elegant bedrooms overlooking the gardens and a luxurious two bedroom cottage, Duck Lodge. The elegant Conservatory is renowned for its fine dining and The Duck Restaurant in restored courtyard buildings offers a more casual alternative.

Marlfield provides the perfect backdrop for exclusive use weddings from 50 to 145, corporate meetings, team building and product launches. Delicious food, luxurious surroundings and impeccable service provide the perfect escape from it all. Best rates are offered for Blue Book vouchers.

2017 Awards:
National Hospitality Ireland Awards: Best Boutique Hotel.
Gold Medal Award: Ireland's Country House.
The Good Hotel Guide: Editor's Choice Country House Hotel.
Michelin Guide, The Duck Restaurant.
La Liste: One of the Best 11 Restaurants in Ireland.
One Fab Day: 100 Best Wedding Venues.

Bedrooms **19**   Gate lodge with 2 bedrooms

Marlfield House, Courtown Road R742, Gorey, Co.Wexford
T +353 (0)53 94 21124
info@marlfieldhouse.ie
www.marlfieldhouse.com

Proprietor: The Bowe Family
General Managers: Margaret and Laura Bowe
Open 1st February to 9th January.
Open all year for weddings and special events.
B&B: Bedrooms from €105 – €128 pps.
State Bedrooms: €190 – €310 pps.
The Gate Lodge from €540 per night.
Three Course Seasonal dinner from €40, Five course €64.
Sunday lunch €45,
Check website for seasonal opening times.

How to find:
Marlfield is 75km south of Dublin off the N11 and is located just outside the town of Gorey on the Courtown Road R742. From Exit 23 on the N11 follow signs for Courtown, at Courtown Road roundabout turn left for Gorey. Follow signs for Marlfield.

GPS coordinates
N 52 40 06
W 06 16 46

THE MERRION HOTEL

HOTEL & RESTAURANT

The Merrion, Dublin's most stylish 5 star hotel is situated opposite Government Buildings in the city centre. Created from four Georgian Townhouses and a contemporary Garden Wing, the 142 bedrooms and suites are arranged around beautifully manicured gardens. Stunningly restored interiors provide the backdrop for one of Ireland's most impressive art collections.

Guests have the choice of two bars and two restaurants, including The Garden Room and the 2 Michelin starred – Restaurant Patrick Guilbaud.

Additional features include Georgian Drawing Rooms where Art Afternoon Tea is served daily, and The Merrion Spa which boasts an 18m pool, gymnasium, steam room and treatment rooms.

The Gold List 2018.
Condé Nast Traveler, USA, December 2017.
Brides Top 100 Venue 2018.
Brides Magazine, Condé Nast, February 2018.

Bedrooms **142**   Hotel ★ ★ ★ ★ ★

The Merrion Hotel,
Upper Merrion Street, Dublin 2
T +353 (0)1 603 0600
info@merrionhotel.com
www.merrionhotel.com

General Manager: Peter MacCann
Published Rates:
From €270 – €3,200 per room, per night.
Subject to availability and season.

GDS Code: LW8430.

How to find:
Located in Dublin city centre on Upper Merrion Street, opposite Government Buildings.

GPS coordinates
Lat: 53.338596
Long: -6.252956

MOUNT JULIET ESTATE

Steeped in heritage, Mount Juliet Estate is one of Ireland's lavish country estates, famed for its welcome and exceptional service.

Overlooking Ballylinch Stud, the 32 bedroom Manor House dates back to the 18th century and offers dining at the 1 Michelin Star Lady Helen Restaurant, golf on the Jack Nicklaus signature course, river & lake fishing, equestrian centre with extensive trails, falconry, woodland walks and much more.

Laid-back luxury is provided with 93 bedrooms at Hunter's Yard, Mount Juliet Estate's original stables and is home to the 2 AA Rosettes restaurant The Hound, The Saddle Bar and the Estate's leisure and spa suites.

Mount Juliet Estate is located 20 minutes from the medieval city of Kilkenny & 90 minutes from Dublin.

The Lady Helen Restaurant – 1 **Michelin** Star & 3 **AA** Rosettes.
The Hound – 2 **AA** Rosettes.

Bedrooms **125**   Luxury Country House & Estate ★ ★ ★ ★

Mount Juliet Country Estate,
Thomastown, Co.Kilkenny
T +353 (0)56 777 3000
info@mountjuliet.ie
www.mountjuliet.ie

General Manager: Mark Dunne
Open all year round.
Manor Executive King, from €240 for room only
Hunter's Yard Classic Double, from €145 room only.

How to find:
From Dublin: Take the N7/M7 (Naas Road) – branch onto the M9, signposted 'Waterford, Carlow & Kilkenny' which is Exit 11 on the M7. Follow the M9 and take Exit 9 signposted 'Kilkenny/Stoneyford'. At the top of the ramp turn left onto the N10 heading for Stoneyford. Drive straight through the village of Stoneyford and at the end of the village at the fork in the road (at the school) take the left hand turn, signposted 'Mount Juliet 4km'. After 4km, Mount Juliet will be on the left.

GPS Coordinates:
N 52° 31' 33.00"
W 07° 11' 13.00"

MOY HOUSE

Moy House is a beautifully restored early 19th century house ideally situated 10 minutes from the Cliffs of Moher on the "Wild Atlantic Way".

9 individually designed bedrooms make Moy House the perfect home away from home offering warm hospitality in contemporary, elegant surroundings.

A dedicated farm to fork approach to food ensures dining at Moy House is a truly memorable experience. 20 acres provide an 'outdoor larder' for the kitchen, rearing pigs, lamb, chickens and beef to serve alongside seasonal vegetables grown in the kitchen gardens.

Located minutes from world famous championships links golf courses, Moy House is a haven for the keen golfer.

Awards include:
2 **AA** Rosettes for Culinary Excellence.
Irish Restaurant awards 2018 – Best Hotel and Guesthouse Restaurant in Clare.
The Irish Times – Top 100 Restaurants in Ireland 2018.

Bedrooms **9**   Guesthouse ★ ★ ★ ★

Moy House, Lahinch, Co.Clare
T +353 (0)65 708 2800
info@moyhouse.com
www.moyhouse.com

Proprietor: Antoin O'Looney
Closed November – March.
Double rooms €145 – €320 per room B&B.
Signature suites €280 – €395 per room B&B.
Special packages also available.
Dinner Menu €65.

How to find:
Moy House is located 1km outside Lahinch on N67 Miltown Malbay Road.

Shannon airport 48km.
Lahinch Golf Course 2km.
Doonbeg Golf Course 28km.

GPS coordinates
Lat: 52.951381
Long: -9.346285

THE MUSTARD SEED

Nestled in the heart of the Golden Vale, overlooking the rustic village of Ballingarry. On the doorstep to Adare, the restaurant is legendary with superb food and quintessential country house hospitality.

Sitting on twelve acres of manicured lawns, orchard and a working kitchen garden, an eclectic, heritage hideaway, the perfect venue for romantic escapes, special occasions and intimate weddings.

The house looks across at Knockfierna, the highest peak in the Mid West landscape, the perfect trek for even the amateur walker. Close to Lough Gur, one of Ireland's finest archaeological and historical gems.

"combines country house luxury with award-winning cuisine, perfect for city-slickers in need of recharging." Amie-Jo Locke, Tatler magazine.

'Best Front of House team' 2018 – **Yeschef.** 'Best Customer Service' 2018 – **RAI.** 'Irish Breakfast Awards 2017' – **Georgina Campbell.** 'Outstanding Guest Experience' 2016 by **Georgina Campbell.** Included in **Trip Advisor's** Hall of Fame. **Onefabday** 100 Best Wedding Venues 2018. **Michelin** recommended.

Bedrooms **17**   Hotel ★ ★ ★ ★

The Mustard Seed,
Ballingarry, Co.Limerick, V94 EHN8
T +353 (0)69 68508
mustard@indigo.ie
www.mustardseed.ie

General Manager: John Edward Joyce
B&B rates: €70 – €165 pps.
Single supplement: From €25.
Classic House menu: €62.
Early Evening Dinner: €48.
Tasting Dinner: €75.
Pets by arrangement.
Children welcome.
Wheelchair friendly.

How to find:
From Limerick: From the top of Adare village, take the N21 Killarney road for half a mile. Turn left at the first road junction to the left and follow the signposts for Ballingarry village.
From Kerry: Travel along the N21. Look for signs for Rathkeale. In Rathkeale town, follow the R518 for four miles to Ballingarry village.

GPS coordinates
Lat: 52.474672
Long: 8.864692

NEWFORGE HOUSE

With beautiful views of gardens and green fields, our lovingly resorted 18th century home, set in 40 acres, offers peace and tranquility. A warm welcome and elegant rooms, with family antiques and modern luxuries, await you.

With only six bedrooms Newforge offers an intimate home from home experience. For breakfast and in our daily changing dinner menu, you will find homegrown fruits, vegetables and eggs from the chickens in our orchard, together with carefully chosen local produce.

Located 30 minutes from Belfast and 90 minutes from Dublin, Newforge is the perfect bolthole for a romantic night away or exploring Northern Ireland.

Awards include:
RAI: Best Hotel Restaurant Ulster 2018.
McKennas' Guides: Top 100 Places to Stay in Ireland 2018.
Tripadvisor Traveller's Choice 2018: Top 20 Small Hotels in UK.
Georgina Campbell Irish Breakfast Awards 2017: National Winner – Guesthouse.

Bedrooms **6**   Guesthouse ★ ★ ★ ★ ★

Newforge House, 58 Newforge Road, Magheralin, Co.Armagh, BT67 0QL
T +44 (0)28 926 11255
enquiries@newforgehouse.com
www.newforgehouse.com

Proprietor: John & Louise Mathers
Open: 1 February – 16 December.
B&B rates: £67.50 – £105 pps.
Single Supplement from £25.
Mid-week, weekend and multiple-night breaks available.
3-Course Dinner £47, served at 8pm Tues – Sat.

How to find:
From Belfast: M1 West, exit 9, Moira follow 5km. In Magheralin left at Byrne's pub: left after national speed limit sign.
From Newry: A1 north towards Belfast. Follow c. 30km, exit Dromore onto B2 (Lurgan Road). Continue 8km, take right onto Newforge Road B9. Continue 1km: 200m on right after bridge.

GPS coordinates
N 54.4619 W -6.2577

NEWPORT HOUSE

A Historic Georgian House in gardens and park adjoining the town and overlooking the Newport river and quay. For two hundred years it was the home of the O'Donnells, once the Earls of Tir Connell.

Famous as an angling centre Newport House offers preserved salmon and sea trout fishing on the Newport river (8 miles) and Lough Beltra.

The cuisine is based on fresh local produce and is complemented by an extensive cellar which includes many of the classical vintages. The house is furnished with many fine antiques and paintings which provide an elegant setting for a quiet and relaxing holiday.

RAI "Best Wine Experience in Connaught 2017".

Bedrooms **10**   Hotel ★ ★ ★ ★

Newport House, Newport, Co.Mayo
T +353 (0)98 41222
info@newporthouse.ie
www.newporthouse.ie

How to find:
In the town of Newport.

Proprietor: Kieran Thompson
Open early April – early October 2019
B&B: from €95.00 – €125.00 Low Season
from €110.00 – €140.00 High Season.
No Single Supplement.
No Service Charge.
5 Course Dinner €68.00 also à la carte – available from 7.00 p.m., to last orders 9.00 p.m. Residents & non-residents.

NO. 1 PERY SQUARE

HOTEL & SPA

Overlooking the handsome, tree-lined Peoples Park in Limerick's historic Georgian Quarter, No.1 Pery Square is a luxurious and intimate boutique town house. Situated just 5 minutes walk from the city centre & train/bus station.

The house comprises of 20 bedrooms all individually named and styled. Delicious food & wine served at Sash and the Park Room lounge. No.1 also houses an organic VOYA spa tucked away in the vaulted cellar and its very own kitchen garden, rooms full of personality and style throughout and a boutique wine shop.

Owner operated and open all year. Guests can enjoy the wonderful Peoples Park, Hunt Museum, King Johns Castle and Riverside walks.

Awards Include:
Conde Nast Hot List Hotel 2009, **Tatler** Best Facial & Boutique Spa Award, **NHA** Best New Hotel 2009, **Gold medal Awards** Best wine experience, **McKenna's Guide** to 100 Best since 2011, Best 100 wedding venues **One Fab Day**, Recommended by **Alistair Sawdays**.

Bedrooms **20**

No. 1 Pery Square Hotel & Spa
Georgian Quarter, Limerick, Ireland
T +353 (0)61 402402
info@oneperysquare.com
www.oneperysquare.com

Proprietor: Patricia Roberts
Club rooms from €75 – €125pps.
Period rooms from €99 – €150pps.
Townhouse Suite €150 – €190pps.
Special Midweek and weekend packages available.
Sash 3 Course Garden Menu from €35 – €49.
Sunday Lunch from €25.

How to find:
Shannon Airport – 27,5 km,
Cork Airport, Dublin Airport – 200km
2 mins walk to O'Connell Street, Bus and train Station. 5 mins walk to Shopping.

GPS coordinates
52° 39' 29.12'' N
8° 37' 48.17'' W

PARK HOTEL KENMARE

Since 1897 many world travellers have enjoyed the pleasure of the Park Hotel Kenmare and its renowned restaurant. Set in a heavenly location overlooking Kenmare Bay the hotel is in the heart of Ireland's most scenic countryside. All accommodations are spacious with sitting area, antique furnishings and original art while Deluxe and Suites enjoy a full sea view or private veranda.

Home to the Deluxe Destination Spa SÁMAS guests can experience the virtues of a true spa. This special and quite unique place blends healing and therapeutic traditions from the East and West with the life inspiring scenery of Kerry to revive the body, mind and soul.

Awards include:
2018 Best Hotel Restaurant in Ireland **Hospitality Awards.**
Best Chef in Kerry 2017 **Restaurant Association Awards.**
Highly Commended Innovation Award **Tatler Spa Awards 2017.**

Bedrooms **43**   Hotel ★ ★ ★ ★ ★

Park Hotel Kenmare, Kenmare, Co.Kerry
T +353 (0)64 664 1200
F +353 (0)64 664 1402
info@parkkenmare.com
www.parkkenmare.com

Managing Director: John Brennan
Closed Jan 2nd – Feb 8th
Closed Dec 15th – 23rd
Open Christmas and Festive season
Double/Twin €145pps – €650pps.
Dinner €75.
Two Night Packages from €345pps.
Wheelchair facilities.
Children welcome.

How to find:
'Top of Town'.

GPS:
N 51.877849
W -9.580554

RATHMULLAN HOUSE COUNTRY HOUSE & RESTAURANT

Situated on the shores of Lough Swilly, a short walk through the rolling front lawn, leads you to a 2 mile golden sandy beach. The interior is relaxed and welcoming with open fires burning in the homely lounges.

Bedrooms range from romantic doubles with garden views to large garret rooms for families. A heated indoor swimming pool provides the perfect opportunity to unwind after a day of sightseeing.

In the Cook & Gardener restaurant, you will find locally sourced produce including Donegal landed seafood. The Tap Room, an informal dining option, offers woodfired pizzas courtesy of Scarpello & Co and locally brewed craft beer from Kinnegar Brewing.

Awards include:
One Fab Day – Top 100 Wedding Venue 2018.
John & Sally McKennas Guide – Top 100 Places to Stay & Eat 2018.
RAI Award – Best Donegal Restaurant 2018.

Bedrooms **32**   Hotel ★ ★ ★ ★

Rathmullan House, Rathmullan, Co.Donegal
T +353 (0)74 915 8188
reception@rathmullanhouse.com
www.rathmullanhouse.com

Proprietor: The Wheeler Family
Open full time from: March to October,
Winter Weekends, Half Terms & New Year.
B&B from €85 – €125 pps low season.
From €110 – €155 pps high season.
Single rooms available at no supplement.
Children welcome, busy with extended families during holiday times.
A la carte dinner available 6pm – 8.30pm.
10% Service charge on extras only.

How to find:
From Letterkenny go to Ramelton (R245) and on to Rathmullan (R247). Turn left at butchers, through village heading north and gates are on the right.

GPS coordinates
N 55.0989383
W 7.53266

RATHSALLAGH HOUSE

Converted from Queen Anne stables in 1798, Rathsallagh is a large comfortable house situated in hundreds of acres of peaceful parkland with a walled garden and surrounded by the magnificent Rathsallagh Golf Club, a championship course measuring in excess of 7,000 yards. Also close to Glendalough, the Wicklow mountains, The National Stud (with its Japanese Gardens) and the Curragh, yet Dublin Airport is less than one hour's drive.

Rathsallagh is renowned for the consistency of its restaurant over the past 30 years, showcasing Irish Country House cooking at its best.

Available for private parties and exclusive rental for all events from family celebrations, weddings, incentives to conferences and meetings catering for up to 250 guests.

Historic Hotel Wedding Experience 2017 – **Historic Hotels of Europe.**
Best Wedding Venue 2017 – **National Hospitality Awards.**
Exclusive Wedding Venue of the Year Ireland 2018 – **Weddings Online.**
Best Customer Service, Wicklow 2017 – **Irish Restaurant Awards.**

Bedrooms **39**

Rathsallagh House, Dunlavin, Co.Wicklow
T +353 (0)45 403112, F +353 (0)45 403343
info@rathsallagh.com
www.rathsallagh.com

Proprietor: The O'Flynn Family
Open all year round.
Bed & Breakfast from €95 pps. Free Wi fi.
Single Supplement from €75.
Dinner from €40.
Open for Sunday lunch.
Prior reservation essential.
Available for private fully serviced rentals.
Site inspections by appointment only.

How to find:
Signposted from Dunlavin.
Less than 50 mins Dublin airport.
M50 for Kildare / South – N7 South.
Exit jct. 11 for M9 south. Exit jct. 3 left signposted.

Established in 1981, Restaurant Patrick Guilbaud is Ireland's top restaurant, holder of two Michelin stars as well as virtually all the top national and international awards. It is situated in an 18th century Georgian Townhouse adjoining the Merrion Hotel. It houses an impressive collection of Irish Art.

This bright, elegant restaurant, run by Stephane Robin, serves modern classic cuisine using the best Irish produce in season. Chef Guillaume Lebrun's signature dishes include the Lobster Ravioli, Roast Challans Duck, Coeur de Guanja, Chocolate Tart.

The wine list is very impressive in both its depth and its range – do take time to peruse it.

Covers **85**

Restaurant Patrick Guilbaud,
21 Upper Merrion Street, Dublin 2
T +353 (0)1 6764 192
info@restaurantpatrickguilbaud.ie
www.restaurantpatrickguilbaud.ie

Proprietor: Patrick Guilbaud
Chef: Guillaume Lebrun
Manager: Stephane Robin
Open: Tuesday to Saturday.
Closed December 25th to January 4th.
Lunch: 12:30 – 2pm. Dinner: 7pm – 10pm.
Lunch Menu: €50 (2 Courses) €60 (3 Courses),
except December.
Special Christmas Lunch Menu €80 for all
December.
Tasting Menu: €195.

Degustation menu €130, available Tuesday to
Thursday.
A la Carte available Lunch & Dinner.
Private Dining Room.

How to find:
Opposite Government buildings.
Merrion Street.

ROSLEAGUE MANOR

A beautifully situated Georgian house overlooking Ballinakill Bay, which has been lovingly converted into a first-class hotel with a Victorian style conservatory and delightful drawing rooms with open log fires. All of the bedrooms are individually decorated and feature fine antiques and paintings.

Set in 30 acres of secluded woodland on the ocean's edge, Rosleague is located just one mile from the Connemara National Park, an area of some 5,000 acres and just 5 minutes drive from Kylemore Abbey and its beautiful walled gardens.

Cuisine is based on the freshest and finest of ingredients, with local seafood and Connemara lamb a speciality.

Sunday Independent – *"As such, Rosleague Manor's Summer Eden is a hard stage to beat."*

One Fab Day – *"A Dazzling Dozen, 12 fabulous new Irish Wedding Venues."*

Tripadvisor – *'Top 10 Best Small Hotels in Ireland.'*

Bedrooms **21**   Listed Heritage Hotel ★ ★ ★ ★

Rosleague Manor, Letterfrack, Connemara, Co.Galway
T +353 (0)95 41101
F +353 (0)95 41168
info@rosleague.com
www.rosleague.com

How to find:
N59, seven miles north west from Clifden.

GPS coordinates
N 53.5514
W 9.9716

Proprietors: Edmund and Mark Foyle
Open: 15 March – 1 November.
B&B from €80 – €125 pps.
Single supplement €36.
2 Course Dinner €36.
5 Course Dinner €50.
Special short break rates on request.
Dog Friendly.
Exclusive residential wedding parties: 100 max.

TANKARDSTOWN

A stunning 18th century Georgian house set in 80 acres of magnificent parkland, comprising superbly restored surrounding courtyards and walled gardens. Guests are offered the opportunity to experience genuine hospitality whilst enjoying the true feel of the quintessential Country House.

Situated in the heart of the Boyne Valley in the Heritage County of Meath. As part of Ireland's Ancient East Tankardstown is just 40 minutes from Dublin City and 30 minutes from Dublin Airport.

Stay in a main house heritage bedroom, or in a beautifully appointed courtyard cottage. Enjoy Lunch and Dinner in award winning Brabazon Restaurant or enjoy Afternoon tea & casual lunch, in The Tea Garden.

Awards include:

AA 5 Gold Star Accommodation 2017; **AA** 2 Rosette Brabazon Restaurant;
Restaurants Association of Ireland: Best Chef in Meath 2016.
Best Business Destination 2018 – **Georgina Campbell Guides.**

Bedrooms **7** (main house)　　**7** Chic Courtyard Cottages　　　Specialist Accommodation/
Failte Ireland's Welcome Standard

**Tankardstown House, Nr. Slane,
Rathkenny, Co.Meath**
T +353 (0)41 982 4621
info@tankardstown.ie
www.tankardstown.ie

Proprietor: Brian & Trish Conroy
Open all year round.
Courtyard Room: €105 pps B&B.
Main House Heritage Bedroom: €335 per room B&B.
Master Suite: €360 per room B&B.

How to find:
From Dublin take the M1 motorway and exit at Junction 10. Follow the signs for Slane. Continue straight through the village on N51 — **or**— Take the N2 which will bring you directly into the village of Slane. Turn left at the traffic lights and continue through the village on N51. Come to main entrance gates to Slane Castle on your left. Directly opposite, turn right, at the fork STAY LEFT, and follow straight along this road for 4km. Signposted 'Tankardstown'.

GPS coordinates
N 53° 44' 27"
W 6° 36' 41"

Since Paul and Máire Flynn opened The Tannery in 1997, it has become one of the most original and welcoming experiences in Irish food. What makes it special? There is Paul's cooking, of course – his fresh Waterford ingredients, ever-changing menus and mouth-watering focus on local produce. There is our unique location in the seaside town of Dungarvan, a stone's throw from the Copper Coast and Comeragh Mountains. The Tannery is the ideal base to stay when exploring the beautiful Waterford Greenway. But most of all, there is the Tannery's knack for serving up that most important of ingredients: a great time.

Staying overnight in the Tannery Townhouse, our compact and cosy rooms in the heart of downtown Dungarvan completes the Tannery experience.

Awards Include:
McKenna Guides 100 Best Places to Eat and 100 Best Places to Stay 2016.
RAI Cookery School of the Year 2016.

Bedrooms **14**   Failte Ireland Welcome Standard 2019

Tannery Restaurant, Townhouse and Cookery School, Dungarvan, Co.Waterford
T +353 (0) 58 45420
info@tannery.ie
www.tannery.ie

How to find:
At end lower Main Street, beside Old Market House Building.
For Tannery Townhouse, please check in at Tannery Restaurant.

Proprietor: Paul and Máire Flynn
Normal Opening Times:
Dinner Tuesday to Saturday.
Lunch Friday and Sunday.
Open Sunday evenings bank holiday weekends and July, August.
Closed two weeks end January, beginning February.
Double rooms from €120 including breakfast.

VIEWMOUNT HOUSE COUNTRY HOUSE & RESTAURANT

Discover this boutique gem, a secret tucked away in the heart of Ireland. This magnificent 17th century country house is complemented by its incredible countryside surroundings, and by the four acres of meticulously-maintained garden that surround it. Within the house you will find open fires, beautiful furniture, fresh flowers and Irish literature. It retains its stately, historic charm, and blends it with thoughtful renovation that incorporates modern comfort.

Enjoy Viewmount's exquisite dining experience - VM Restaurant is candlelit, with exposed stone walls, contemporary paintings, linen tablecloths. It is these aspects with the impeccable service, that create a superb atmosphere in which to relax.

Awards include:

Georgina Campbell Guide: "Hospitality Hero" Award 2018.
Country House of the Year 2017.
Good Hotel Guide: César Award, Best Irish Hotel Winner 2018.
John & Sally Mc Kenna's Guide.
One Fab Day Best 100 Wedding Venues.

Bedrooms **12**   Guesthouse ★ ★ ★ ★

Viewmount House
Dublin Road, Longford, N39 N2X6
T + 353 (0)43 3341919
info@viewmounthouse.com
www.viewmounthouse.com

Proprietor: Beryl & James Kearney
Closed 27 October – 6 November 2019.
Closed 24 – 27 December 2019.
Bed & Breakfast: €80.00 – €120.00pps.
Restaurant:
Open Wed. to Sat.: 6.30pm to 9.00pm.
Early Menu (Wed. & Thurs.): €37.50 – €40.00.
5 Course Dinner: €65.00 – €70.00.
Lunch (Sunday only) 1.00pm to 4.00pm: €35.00.
All major credit cards accepted.

How to find:
From Dublin: Take M4 / N4 (Sligo). At the first roundabout entering Longford town, take first exit. Continue for .75km., sign for Viewmount House and VM Restaurant is on the left. Turn left at this junction). Continue for approx 800m and entrance is on the right.
Longford town centre:
Take R393 (Ardagh), drive 1km and take the first slip road to the right, 800m, entrance is on the right.

GPS coordinates
53.72246
-7.77105

An 18th century hunting estate set in 100 acres of beautiful countryside overlooking Lough Ramor. Truly a unique estate and former home of Lord Headfort and his wife, the Marchioness of Headfort.

The property has been brought back to life and into the Irish hands of Chef Richard Corrigan – one of the most established Irish chefs in the UK and beyond; also operating his flagship London restaurant Corrigan's in Mayfair and the 101 year old Bentley's Oyster Bar & Grill in Piccadilly.

The stunning estate is a haven for walkers, fishermen, boaters and those simply looking to relax in serene beauty of the Irish countryside.

Awards include:
Richard has gained 2 **Michelin** Stars in his career along with winning 3 **AA** Restaurant of the Year Awards for his London restaurants.
Georgina Campbell: Country House of the Year 2018
The Cateys: 2018 Restauranteur of the Year

Bedrooms **23 Lodge rooms 12 Woodland Huts**

Virginia Park Lodge
Virginia, Co. Cavan, Ireland, A82 T2N6
T +353 (0)49 854 6100
info@virginiaparklodge.com
www.virginiaparklodge.com

Proprietor: Richard Corrigan
Woodland Huts from €183.
Lodge Rooms & Suites from €220.

How to find:
Coming from Virginia town, head northwest. Take a slight left onto Ballyjamesduff Road. Continue for 250 metres, then turn left.

GPS coordinates
Latitude: 53.834777
Longitude: -7.093105

WINEPORT LODGE

Hidden under leafy shade, with lawns that flow to the lapping waters of Lough Ree, is a secret hideaway. A haven of natural beauty and cosy, laid back luxury, Wineport Lodge has style and seclusion in perfect balance. Dine, delight and dream in blissful comfort.

Guest facilities include Treatment Suite and Hot Tub. Bikes rides, boat trips and woodland walks that start right at the door. Glasson village with its traditional pubs, craft shop and gallery is a stroll away.

TripAdvisor Travellers Choice Awards 2017 Top 25 Romantic Hotels in Ireland.

'Imagine a secluded wooden hotel built on the edge of a beautiful lake, with windows facing west; balconies on which to drink in the heavenly, endlessly changing views; wood-burning stoves; superb cuisine – and a delightfully relaxed vibe. That's Wineport!,' Neil Hegarty, The Telegraph.

Food and Wine Awards Best for Romance Award 2018.

Bedrooms / Suites **30**

Hotel ★ ★ ★ ★

**Wineport Lodge, Glasson,
Athlone, Co.Westmeath**
T +353 (0)90 643 9010
lodge@wineport.ie
www.wineport.ie

Proprietors: Ray Byrne and Jane English
Open all year round.
Closed 24 – 26 December.
Rooms from €85 pps B&B.
Suites from €110 pps B&B.
Afternoon tea from €30pp.
All Day Dining Menu.
A La Carte Dinner Menu.
Sunday Lunch (4 course): €39 pp.

How to find:
Take exit 10 off M6/N6 Dublin-Galway.
Follow N55 direction Cavan. At Ballykeeran fork left at Dog & Duck pub. Then 1.6 kilometres (1 mile) on left hand side.

GPS coordinates
N 53.465161
W -7.884579

THE HIDEAWAY AT DROMQUINNA MANOR

Perched atop a wooded cliff, The Hideaway is nothing short of a luxurious escape and surrender to nature.

Leave everyday life as you know it behind and reconnect with yourself and a loved one for an experience unlike any other. The view from your veranda is simply breathtakingly gorgeous. The blue waters of the Atlantic Gulf Stream lap the shoreline beneath as you sit in your Adirondack chair where the only, occasional, interruption is a graceful flyby by your resident neighbour, The Heron. Everyday life is on hold like never before.

The Hideaway is the ultimate in luxury camping. In reality it is not camping at all but a luxurious en-suite bedroom in its own private grounds on an estate like no other. BBQ or dine in The Boathouse for dinner while a breakfast basket is delivered to your door each morning.

Welcome to another world, The Hideaway at Dromquinna Manor.

The Hideaway, Dromquinna Manor, Kenmare, Co Kerry, V93 AY24
T +353 (0)64 66 42888
admin@dromquinnamanor.com
www.dromquinnamanor.com

Proprietors: John & Gwen Brennan
Available nightly from May-September.
Adults Only.
Rates: €350 per night.
Multi night packages available.

How to find:
5km from Kenmare on the N70.

GPS coordinates
N 51.870462
W -9.64322

DUNOWEN HOUSE

Dunowen House is a luxury 18th Century property on the Wild Atlantic Way, close to Clonakilty. Surrounded by private coves and beaches, guests get the chance to totally experience West Cork.

Carefully restored, it showcases its unique rock and roll heritage, as the former home of Noel Redding, bass guitarist with the Jimi Hendrix Experience. A music room is dedicated to memorabilia, vintage posters and music magazines.

When you stay it is yours exclusively - ideal for families, friends, celebrations and events. Dunowen offers the comforts of a luxury small hotel with the privacy of a country estate. Private catering available.

Awards:

John & Sally McKenna's Guide – Best Places to Stay 2016, 2017, 2018.
Pól O'Conghaile, The Independent – The Fab 50: Best Places to stay in Ireland 2018.
The Vow, wedding magazine – Best Places to Hen Party like Meghan Markle, 2018.

Main House **6 suites**, max 18 guests.
Orchard Cottage, **2 double, 1 single**, max 5 guests.

Dunowen House
Ardfield, Clonakilty, Co. Cork
T +353 (0)23 886 9099
info@dunowenhouse.ie
www.dunowenhouse.ie

Proprietors: Kela & Stephen Hodgins
Open: All year round (serviced self-catering).
Min stay 2 nights, except June – August min 7 nights.
Weekend Celebration 2 night stay & dinner party from €165 pps.
2 night self-catering from €1,700.
Weekly rates:
Low Season: €3,200 – €4,000.
High Season: €3,600 – €5,000.
Christmas, New Year & Easter: €3,400 – €4,500.

For weddings, celebrations, corporate or wellness retreats, please contact us for rates.

How to find:
We are located at Sands Cove, 10km from Clonakilty, on the Wild Atlantic Way through Ardfield.
From Cork Airport – 50 mins
From Dublin Airport – 3.5 hours
From Shannon Airport – 2.5 hours

GPS coordinates
51.556038
-8.905305

KILLADANGAN HOUSE

Killadangan House is a beautifully restored and elegantly furnished period property with panoramic sea views overlooking Clew Bay, 5km from Westport town.

We offer luxurious self catering accommodation with superb facilities and comfort. Killadangan House is available on an exclusive, sole occupancy basis, whether your group has 2 or 10 people. We are just minutes from Blue Flag beaches, the Great Western Greenway and Croagh Patrick, as well as the superb restaurants, cafes, pubs and shops of historic Westport town.

A stunning property for families and friends looking for the space and grandeur of a period country house but with the privacy and flexibility of self catering.

Bedrooms **2 double, 3 twin**   Failte Ireland Welcome standard

---

Killadangan House
Killadangan, Westport, Co Mayo
T +353 (0)87 165 0570
info@killadanganhouse.com
www.killadanganhouse.com

Proprietors: The Fischer Family
Manager: Rachel Guthrie
Open All Year Round (serviced self catering)
Minimum 2 night stay.
The rate varies depending on the number of guests in the group.
Cleaning charge applies, all other costs included.
Low season €300 (2 guests) – €700 (10 guests) per night.
High season €400 (2 guests) – €800 (10 guests) per night.
Christmas and New Year, contact for rates.

How to find:
We are 5k from Westport town on the direct coast road to Louisburgh R335.
From Knock Airport: 63km (39 miles) – 50 minutes.
From Galway: 80km (49 miles) – 1.5hrs.
From Sligo: 104km (65 miles) –1.5hrs.
From Dublin: 252km (156 miles) – 3.5hrs.
From Belfast: 305km (190 miles) – 4.15hrs.

GPS coordinates
Geographic coordinates
53.780884
- 9.599057

The Shannon Princess is a luxury boutique hotel barge cruising the river Shannon in Ireland. Family run and with a professional crew, the Shannon Princess is the perfect way to explore what the river and her loughs have to offer. Guests on board will enjoy all the indulgent comforts of their own private floating luxury hotel, an unforgettable experience that will create memories forever.

Cruises are of a 6 night / 7 day duration, which can be booked by the cabin or as an exclusive Charter for up to 10 guests. Itineraries choices include Classic, Walking, Golf and Family Cruises. On board contemporary luxury seamlessly blends with a welcoming atmosphere and casual informality. Deluxe accommodations include Air Conditioning, a deck side Spa pool and delicious cuisine and wines.

Bedrooms **5 ensuite cabins**

Shannon Princess, Glasson, Athlone, Co.Westmeath
T +353 (0)87 2514809
info@shannonprincess.com
www.shannonprincess.com

Proprietor: The Gibbons Family
Low/Value Season – Apr 21st to May 5th
Suite (per person, double occupancy): $4,600
Suite Single Supplement: $1,600
Charter for 10:: $43,900
Charter for 8: $41,600
Charter for 6: $39,300
High Season – May 12th to Sept 22nd
Suite (per person, double occupancy): $5350
Suite Single Supplement: $1,800

Charter for 10:	$49,500
Charter for 8:	$46,800
Charter for 6:	$43,800

How to find:
Departures are from Glasson, Athlone to Killaloe and every second week from Killaloe to Glasson.

HeritageISLAND
IRELAND'S PREMIER ATTRACTIONS

Museums **Historic Houses** Gardens
Distilleries Heritage Towns **Caves**
Interpretative Centres **Family Days Out**
Castles Suggested Tour Itineraries

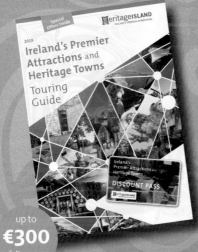

up to
€300
of discounts **at Ireland's leading visitor attractions.**

Guides & Discount Pass, On-line Tickets & Events
details available at
www.heritageisland.com

**Visitor
Attractions Guides**

**Discount
Pass**

**TopAttractions
Ireland.com**

SOMETHING
EXTRAORDINARY
EVERY DAY™

Discover 100 boutiques, all offering savings of up to 60%‡ on your shopping.

Present this page at Tourist Information, before September 2019, to receive a VIP Card for an additional 10% off* the Village price.

Terms and conditions apply. Not valid in conjunction with any other offers at Kildare Village. Offer valid until September 2019.

KILDARE VILLAGE

A MEMBER OF THE BICESTER VILLAGE SHOPPING COLLECTION®

Russborough
HOUSE & PARKLANDS

WHERE HISTORY & CULTURE LIVE ON

Russborough is home to one of the most impressive private art collections in Ireland, including Gainsborough, Singer Sargent and van Ostade, which may be viewed by taking a guided tour of the house.

 ## COME VISIT US!

The Beit Museum:
The Beit Museum, opened in 2014, offers a fascinating insight into the history, lives and stories of Russborough and its owners from the 18th century to the present day.

*

The 18th Century walled garden is available for pre booked tours.

*

3km Walking Tour of the Demesne

*

Gift Shop & Restaurant

*

For Family Fun there is a Maze, Fairy trail, Playground & Tree trail

Tel: + 353 (0)45 865239
Email:
friedaoconnell@russborough.ie
www.russborough.ie
Sat Nav GPS:
Lat 53.135517
Long 6.572386

 IRELAND'S ANCIENT EAST®
Wonder Through Time

 tripadvisor

* Free Coach Park
* €2 Car Park

Location:
20 km from Dublin
off the N81 and 4.5
km from Blessington
Co. Wicklow, Ireland

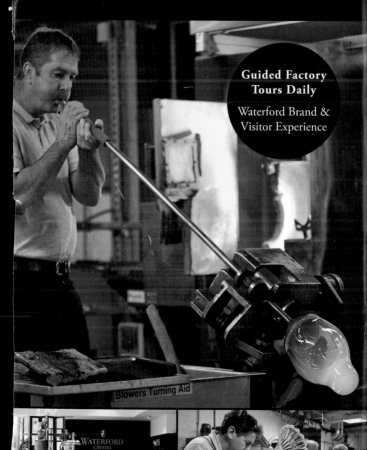

Each house or restaurant has a reference number which relates to both the map opposite and the page on which it appears.

1. **Aherne's Townhouse**
   Tel: +353 (0)24 92424
   E-mail: info@ahernes.net

2. **Ardtara Country House & Restaurant**
   Tel: +44 (0)28 796 44490
   From Republic: 048 796 44490
   E-mail: info@ardtara.com

3. **Ballyfin Demesne**
   Tel: +353 (0)57 875 5866
   E-mail: reservations@ballyfin.com

4. **Ballymaloe House**
   Tel: +353 (0)21 465 2531
   E-mail: res@ballymaloe.ie

5. **Barberstown Castle**
   Tel: +353 (0)1 628 8157
   E-mail: info@barberstowncastle.ie

6. **Belleek Castle**
   Tel: +353 (0) 96 22 400
   E-mail: info@belleekcastle.eu

7. **Bishop's Gate Hotel**
   Tel: +44 (0)28 711 40300
   From Republic: 048 711 40300
   E-mail: sales@bishopsgatehotelderry.com

8. **Blairscove Restaurant and Accommodation**
   Tel: +353 (0)27 61127
   E-mail: mail@blairscove.ie

9. **Bushmills Inn**
   Tel: +44 (0)28 207 33000
   From Republic: 048 207 33000
   E-mail: info@bushmillsinn.com

10. **Butler House**
    Tel: +353 (0)56 7722828
    E-mail: res@butler.ie

11. **Cahernane House Hotel**
    Tel: +353 (0)64 663 1895
    E-mail: info@cahernane.com

12. **Campagne Restaurant**
    Tel: +353 (0)56 777 2858
    E-mail: info@campagne.ie

13. **Carrig Country House & Restaurant**
    Tel: +353 (0)66 976 9100
    E-mail: info@carrighouse.com

14. **Cashel House Hotel**
    Tel: +353 (0)95 31001
    E-mail: sales@cashelhouse.ie

15. **Castle Durrow**
    Tel: +353 (0)57 873 6555
    E-mail: info@castledurrow.com

16. **Castle Grove Country House**
    Tel: +353 (0)74 91 51118
    E-mail: stay@castlegrove.com

17. **Castle Leslie Estate**
    Tel   +353 (0)47 88100
    E-mail: info@castleleslie.com

18. **Chapter One Restaurant**
    Tel: +353 (0)1 873 2266
    E-mail: info@chapteronerestaurant.com

19. **Clare Island Lighthouse**
    Tel: +353 (0)87 668 9758
    E-mail: info@clareislandlighthouse.com

20. **Coopershill House**
    Tel: +353 (0)71 916 5108
    E-mail: ohara@coopershill.com

21. **Currarevagh House**
    Tel: +353 (0)91 552312
    E-mail: rooms@currarevagh.com

22. **Dunbrody House**
    Tel: +353 (0)51 389600
    E-mail: info@dunbrodyhouse.com

23. **Enniscoe House**
    Tel: +353 (0)96 31112
    E-mail: mail@enniscoe.com

24. **Ghan House**
    Tel: +353 (0)42 937 3682
    E-mail: info@ghanhouse.com

25. **Glenlo Abbey Hotel**
    Tel: +353 (0)91 519600
    E-mail: stay@glenloabbey.ie

26. **Gregans Castle Hotel**
    Tel: +353 (0)65 707 7005
    E-mail: stay@gregans.ie

27. **Hayfield Manor**
    Tel: +353 (0)21 484 5900
    E-mail: enquiries@hayfieldmanor.ie

28. **Hunter's Hotel**
    Tel: +353 (0)404 40106
    E-mail: reception@hunters.ie

29. **Ice House**
    Tel: +353 (0)96 23500
    E-mail: chill@theicehouse.ie

30. **Killarney Royal**
    Tel: +353 (0)64 6631853
    E-mail: reception@killarneyroyal.ie

31. **King Sitric Fish Restaurant & Accommodation**
    Tel: +353 (0)1 832 5235
    E-mail: reservations@kingsitric.ie

32. **L'Ecrivain Restaurant**
    Tel: +353 (0)1 661 1919
    E-mail: enquiries@lecrivain.com

33. **Liss Ard Estate**
    Tel: +353 (0)28 40000
    E-mail: reservations@lissard.com

34. **Longueville House**
    Tel: +353 (0)22 47156
    E-mail: info@longuevillehouse.ie

35. **Marlfield House**
    Tel: +353 (0)53 94 21124
    E-mail: info@marlfieldhouse.ie

36. **Merrion Hotel**
    Tel: +353 (0)1 603 0600
    E-mail: info@merrionhotel.com

37. **Mount Juliet Hotel & Estate**
    Tel: +353 (0)56 777 3000
    E-mail: info@mountjuliet.ie

38. **Moy House**
    Tel: +353 (0)65 708 2800
    E-mail: info@moyhouse.com

39. **The Mustard Seed**
    Tel: +353 (0)69 68508
    E-mail: mustard@indigo.ie

40. **Newforge House**
    Tel: +44 (0)28 926 11255
    From Republic: 048 926 11255
    E-mail: enquiries@newforgehouse.com

41. **Newport House**
    Tel: +353 (0)98 41222
    E-mail: info@newporthouse.ie

42. **No. 1 Pery Square**
    Tel: +353 (0)61 402402
    E-mail: info@oneperysquare.com

43. **Park Hotel Kenmare**
    Tel: +353 (0)64 664 1200
    E-mail: info@parkkenmare.com

44. **Rathmullan House**
    Tel: +353 (0)74 915 8188
    E-mail: reception@rathmullanhouse.com

45. **Rathsallagh House**
    Tel: +353 (0)45 403112
    E-mail: info@rathsallagh.com

46. **Restaurant Patrick Guilbaud**
    Tel: +353 (0)1 6764 192
    E-mail: info@restaurantpatrickguilbaud.ie

47. **Rosleague Manor**
    Tel: +353 (0)95 41101
    E-mail: info@rosleague.com

48. **Tankardstown House**
    Tel: +353 (0)41 982 4621
    E-mail: info@tankardstown.ie

49. **The Tannery**
    Tel: +353 (0) 58 45420
    E-mail: info@tannery.ie

50. **Viewmount House**
    Tel: + 353 (0)43 334 1919
    E-mail: info@viewmounthouse.com

51. **Virginia Park Lodge**
    Tel: +353 (0)49 854 6100
    E-mail: info@virginiaparklodge.com

52. **Wineport Lodge**
    Tel: +353 (0)90 643 9010
    E-mail: lodge@wineport.ie

53. **The Hideaway, Dromquinna Manor**
    Tel: +353 (0)64 66 42888
    E-mail: admin@dromquinnamanor.com

54. **Dunowen House**
    Tel: +353 (0)23 886 9099
    E-mail: info@dunowenhouse.ie

55. **Killadangan House**
    Tel: +353 (0)87 165 0570
    E-mail: info@killadanganhouse.com

56. **Shannon Princess**
    Tel: +353 (0)87 2514809
    E-mail: info@shannonprincess.com